CONTENTS

Bottom Line Books® publishes the advice of expert authorities in many fields. These opinions may at times conflict as there are often different approaches to solving problems. The use of this material is no substitute for health, legal, accounting or other professional services. Consult competent professionals for answers to your specific questions.

Telephone numbers, addresses, prices, offers and websites listed in this book are accurate at the time of publication, but they are subject to frequent change.

Bottom Line Books® is a registered trademark of Bottom Line Inc.
3 Landmark Square, Suite 201, Stamford, CT 06901

www.bottomlineinc.com

Bottom Line Books is an imprint of Bottom Line Inc., publisher of print periodicals, e-letters and books. We are dedicated to bringing you the best information from the most knowledgeable sources in the world. Our goal is to help you gain greater wealth, better health, more wisdom, extra time and increased happiness.

Printed in the United States of America

DDC/am

How to Use This Daily Planner to Keep Track of Your Success

You've read *The 30-Day Diabetes Cure* and understand what causes diabetes, what exacerbates it, and what helps reverse it. This foundation will serve you well in the weeks, months, and years ahead. Now you're ready to begin *The 30-Day Diabetes Success Planner*. By following this step-by-step plan you will begin to normalize your blood sugar levels and significantly improve your overall health in just 30 days.

The truth is, we couldn't be happier for you. We want to provide you with the tools you need to succeed. And we want to be with you every step of the way. That's why we created *The 30-Day Diabetes Cure Success Planner.*

This *Success Planner* is a place for you to monitor your progress throughout the plan's 30 days. More than that, though, it helps to reinforce each step within the Plan and encourages you to think about the changes you are making throughout the 30 days—and beyond.

THE SUCCESS PLANNER: STEP-BY-STEP

Today's Action Steps. Every day in the *Success Planner* begins with a detailed list of the day's Action Steps. This list sets the tone, helping you to quickly identify the goals for a particular day.

My Healing Foods Log. My Healing Foods Log is a place for you to record your healthful meals throughout each day.

My Smart Monitoring Results. The chart in this section is a convenient location for you to record your blood glucose readings after using smart monitoring. It is a place to see how specific exercises and food affect your blood glucose levels.

My Daily Activity. Beginning with Day 6, My Daily Activity Log is the spot to record additional activities you incorporate into your daily routine, such as walking, biking or dancing.

My Diabetes-Healing Checklist. Use the My Diabetes-Healing Checklist to record the important steps outlined in the Plan that you have completed that day.

My Insights for Today. Use the My Insights for Today section to write down valuable information related to your daily readings, including your stress level, mood and what foods you ate or activity you did before taking a reading. This is also a place to reflect on the 30-Day Plan and the changes it brings.

Test Your Blood Glucose IQ. A variety of question types in this section will test what you've learned in The 30-Day Diabetes Cure Plan. The key can be found on page 138.

....

You are about to embark on a 30-day plan that will change your life. Congratulations! Each day will bring you one step closer to reversing your diabetes, getting off your medications, and leading a more healthful life. Approach each day with the same commitment and desire to improve your health that you have at this very moment. That's all it takes for you to succeed with this plan.

Here's to you stabilizing your blood sugar and taking control of your health. We know you can do it!

Keep getting better!

Jim Healthy
January 2016

DAY 1: SMART MONITORING

Today's Action Steps:

- Stock up on lancets and test strips. Find the smallest lancet size that works for you.

- Ask yourself how a specific food or activity affects your blood glucose levels, and use smart monitoring to find the answer.

- Familiarize yourself with the logs and start recording your food, activity, and stress levels.

			My Healing Foods Log			
MEALS	**GRAINS**	**VEGETABLES**	**FRUITS**	**DAIRY**	**MEAT**	**OILS**
	Whole grains/slow starches	Organic or on the Clean 15 list*	Organic or on the Clean 15 list	Grass-fed omega-3 milk & healthy dairy alternatives	Grass-fed free-range	Coconut or other high-quality oil
Breakfast						
Lunch						
Dinner						

* Visit *www.ewg.org/foodnews* to obtain the Environmental Working Group's Shopper's Guide.

My Smart Monitoring Results:

Record your smart monitoring results in the chart below.

Smart Monitoring Chart					
Time	Blood Glucose Levels	Insulin Doses	Foods Eaten Before	Recent Activities	Notes About Stress, New Medications, and Emotions

My Diabetes-Healing Checklist:

■ Use smart monitoring to track your blood glucose.

My Insights for Today:

Think about what you did and how you felt today. What foods did you eat before you took your readings? What were your stress levels like at the time? Were you active before your readings? Write your thoughts below.

_____

_____

_____

_____

_____

_____

_____

_____

_____

_____

_____

_____

_____

_____

_____

Test Your Blood Glucose IQ

Multiple Choice: Circle the letter that best answers the question.

1. The best way to monitor your blood glucose levels is to:

    A. Test twice daily, log your blood glucose levels, and show these to your doctor on your next visit.

    B. Test your blood glucose levels when you feel unwell.

    C. Test with purpose before and after meals, snacks and activities in order to see how different foods and activities affect your blood glucose levels.

    D. Only test your blood glucose levels when you think of it.

2. All of the following can raise blood glucose levels, except:

    A. Medications

    B. Poor sleep or sleep apnea

    C. Beverages, such as juice, soda and sports drinks

    D. Adequate amounts of pure water

True or False: For each statement, circle True or False.

3.	It is enough to test your blood glucose levels once a day.	**True**	**False**
4.	The best lancet size is the thinnest that can draw enough blood.	**True**	**False**
5.	Stress can raise your blood glucose levels	**True**	**False**

Fill in the Blank: Write the term that correctly completes the sentence.

logging   **fuel**   **blood glucose levels**   **testing in pairs**   **hunger**

6. A synonym for *smart monitoring* is _____.

7. Careful _____ of your blood glucose will allow you to identify patterns in the way food, medications, sleep, work, and exercise affect your levels.

8. Smart monitoring will help you answer questions about how exercise, food, stress, and medicine affect your _____.

DAY 2: SODAS AND ALCOHOL SWAP

Today's Action Steps:

■ Replace sodas and other sugary drinks with diabetes-healing beverages.

■ Take a 10-day break from alcohol.

■ Purchase a glass or stainless-steel water bottle. Keep it close and full of filtered water.

My Healing Foods Log						
MEALS	**GRAINS**	**VEGETABLES**	**FRUITS**	**DAIRY**	**MEAT**	**OILS**
	Whole grains/slow starches	Organic or on the Clean 15 list (see page 1)	Organic or on the Clean 15 list	Grass-fed omega-3 milk & healthy dairy alternatives	Grass-fed free-range	Coconut or other high-quality oil
Breakfast						
Lunch						
Dinner						

My Smart Monitoring Results:

Record your smart monitoring results in the chart below.

Smart Monitoring Chart					
Time	Blood Glucose Levels	Insulin Doses	Foods Eaten Before	Recent Activities	Notes About Stress, New Medications, and Emotions

My Diabetes-Healing Checklist:

❑ Use smart monitoring to track your blood glucose.
❑ Swap sodas with diabetes-healing beverages.

My Insights for Today:

Think about what you did and how you felt today. What foods did you eat before you took your readings? What were your stress levels like at the time? Were you active before your readings?

How much of a challenge do you feel giving up sodas and alcohol will be? Which diabetes-healing drinks are you the most excited about trying? Write your thoughts below.

_____

_____

_____

_____

_____

_____

_____

_____

_____

_____

_____

_____

_____

_____

Test Your Blood Glucose IQ

Multiple Choice: Circle the letter that best answers the question.

1. Soda affects your health in all the following ways except:

    A. Spikes blood glucose

    B. Contributes to obesity

    C. Slims your waistline and buttocks

    D. Increase your body's aging process

2. Diabetes-healing beverages include all of the following except:

    A. Water with fresh-squeezed lemon

    B. Fruit juice

    C. Unsweetened coffee, black and green tea

    D. Milk

True or False: For each statement, circle True or False.

3. Alcohol is loaded with sugar.   **True**   **False**

4. Orange juice is not a sugary drink.   **True**   **False**

5. Diabetes causes dehydration.   **True**   **False**

Fill in the Blank: Write the term that correctly completes the sentence.

added sweeteners   **pomegranate**   **nutritional value**   **glucose load**

6. Steep your tea in piping hot water for 10 minutes. Never boil your tea, as this destroys its _____.

7. The juice of _____ diluted in sparkling water will not raise your blood glucose.

8. Eliminating soda from your diet will reduce the _____ on your body and allow for the better utilization of insulin.

DAY 3: FRUIT SWAP

Today's Action Steps:

■ Stock your kitchen with a variety of fruits.

MEALS	GRAINS	VEGETABLES	FRUITS	DAIRY	MEAT	OILS
				My Healing Foods Log		
	Whole grains/slow starches	Organic or on the Clean 15 list (see page 1)	Organic or on the Clean 15 list	Grass-fed omega-3 milk & healthy dairy alternatives	Grass-fed free-range	Coconut or other high-quality oil
Breakfast						
Lunch						
Dinner						

My Smart Monitoring Results:

Record your smart monitoring results in the chart below.

Smart Monitoring Chart					
Time	Blood Glucose Levels	Insulin Doses	Foods Eaten Before	Recent Activities	Notes About Stress, New Medications, and Emotions

My Diabetes-Healing Checklist:

❑ Use smart monitoring to track your blood glucose.
❑ Swap sodas with diabetes-healing beverages.
❑ Eat diabetes-healing fruits and berries.

My Insights for Today:

Think about what you did and how you felt today. What foods did you eat before you took your readings? What were your stress levels like at the time? Were you active before your readings?

Which fruits did you stock your kitchen with? Are fruits a regular part of your diet? Why or why not? Write your thoughts below.

_____

_____

_____

_____

_____

_____

_____

_____

_____

_____

_____

_____

_____

Test Your Blood Glucose IQ

Multiple Choice: Circle the letter that best answers the question.

1. Whole, fresh fruit contains which of the following benefits?

    A. Fiber

    B. Vitamins and minerals

    C. Antioxidants

    D. All of the above

2. Fruits to avoid include all of the following except:

    A. Melons

    B. Grapefruit

    C. Papaya

    D. Pineapple

True or False: For each statement, circle True or False.

3. Fruits that have a high Glycemic Index rating should be avoided.   **True   False**

4. Fructose in fruit juice does not contribute to insulin spikes.   **True   False**

5. Combining fruit with proteins reduces the insulin-spiking effect
    of fructose.   **True   False**

Fill in the Blank: Write the term that correctly completes the sentence.

HFCS	**free radicals**	**fruit**	**diabetes-healing**	**avoid**

6. Grapefruit, oranges, blueberries, avocadoes, apples, cherries, cranberries, and
    grapes are all _____ fruits.

7. Antioxidants found in diabetes-healing fruits neutralize inflammation-causing
    _____ present in the body.

8. Jams and jellies, canned and jarred, are forms of _____ to
    _____ because of their sugars and low fiber content.

DAY 4: TAKE A BREAK FROM SWEETS

Today's Action Steps:

■ Begin to break from your sugar dependency today.

■ Eat a little extra protein with your three regularly spaced meals in order to reduce your cravings for sweets.

			My Healing Foods Log			
MEALS	**GRAINS**	**VEGETABLES**	**FRUITS**	**DAIRY**	**MEAT**	**OILS**
	Whole grains/slow starches	Organic or on the Clean 15 list (see page 1)	Organic or on the Clean 15 list	Grass-fed omega-3 milk & healthy dairy alternatives	Grass-fed free-range	Coconut or other high-quality oil
Breakfast						
Lunch						
Dinner						

My Smart Monitoring Results:

Record your smart monitoring results in the chart below.

Smart Monitoring Chart					
Time	Blood Glucose Levels	Insulin Doses	Foods Eaten Before	Recent Activities	Notes About Stress, New Medications, and Emotions

My Diabetes-Healing Checklist:

- ❑ Use smart monitoring to track your blood glucose.
- ❑ Swap sodas with diabetes-healing beverages.
- ❑ Eat diabetes-healing fruits and berries.
- ❑ Swap sugar with stevia.

My Insights for Today:

Think about what you did and how you felt today. What foods did you eat before you took your readings? What were your stress levels like at the time? Were you active before your readings?

Where in your diet have you been consuming the most sugar? How do you feel about taking a break from sweets? Does 3–10 days to break your sugar addiction seem like a reachable goal? Write your thoughts below.

_____

_____

_____

_____

_____

_____

_____

_____

_____

_____

_____

Test Your Blood Glucose IQ

Multiple Choice: Circle the letter that best answers the question.

1.   The best way to deal with your diabetes is to:

     A. Manage blood sugar levels through use of drugs and medications.

     B. Eliminate sugar from your diet and incorporate a healthful lifestyle.

     C. Indulge in highly-processed foods and sugary treats.

     D. Ingest more lead in order to emulate ancient Roman society.

2.   The worst snack to reach for when you crave sugar is:

     A. Cheese

     B. Fresh vegetables

     C. A hydrating beverage, such as hot tea or water

     D. A vending machine packaged snack

True or False: For each statement, circle True or False.

3.   "Cutting back" is the best method for breaking any type of substance addiction.   **True   False**

4.   Sugar is *poison* in the amounts we consume.   **True   False**

5.   Sugar is far less addictive than cocaine.   **True   False**

Fill in the Blank: Write the term that correctly completes the sentence.

   appetite   fuel   leptin   activity   hunger

6.   Glucose is the primary _____ used by cancer cells, which hijack 95% of the glucose intended for healthy body function.

7.   _____ is the desire or craving for a specific food.

8.   _____ is the genuine physiological need for nourishment.

DAY 5: EAT BREAKFAST EVERY DAY

Today's Action Steps:

■ Swap fast-carb breakfasts with protein-rich, diabetes-healing breakfasts.

■ Incorporate high-quality protein and healthful fats in your breakfasts.

My Healing Foods Log						
MEALS	**GRAINS**	**VEGETABLES**	**FRUITS**	**DAIRY**	**MEAT**	**OILS**
	Whole grains/slow starches	Organic or on the Clean 15 list (see page 1)	Organic or on the Clean 15 list	Grass-fed omega-3 milk & healthy dairy alternatives	Grass-fed free-range	Coconut or other high-quality oil
Breakfast						
Lunch						
Dinner						

My Smart Monitoring Results:

Record your smart monitoring results in the chart below.

Smart Monitoring Chart					
Time	Blood Glucose Levels	Insulin Doses	Foods Eaten Before	Recent Activities	Notes About Stress, New Medications, and Emotions

My Diabetes-Healing Checklist:

❑ Use smart monitoring to track your blood glucose.
❑ Swap sodas with diabetes-healing beverages.
❑ Eat diabetes-healing fruits and berries.
❑ Swap sugar with stevia.
❑ Eat a protein-rich breakfast today.

My Insights for Today:

Think about what you did and how you felt today. What foods did you eat before you took your readings? What were your stress levels like at the time? Were you active before your readings?

Is breakfast part of your daily routine? What can you do to make sure you are up early enough to make breakfast each morning or have a healthful breakfast prepared in advance? What diabetes-healing breakfast will you try first? Write your thoughts below.

_____

_____

_____

_____

_____

_____

_____

_____

_____

_____

Test Your Blood Glucose IQ

Multiple Choice: Circle the letter that best answers the question.

1. A diabetes-healing breakfast is built around:

   A. Carb-rich foods like boxed cereal and bagels

   B. A 20oz, sugar-laden latte

   C. High-quality protein, such as eggs, yogurt or nut butter

   D. All of the above

2. Eating a healthful breakfast every day will result in:

   A. Stabilized blood glucose levels

   B. Reduced cravings for sweet, fast-carb snacks

   C. Lessen "brain fog"

   D. All of the above

True or False: For each statement, circle True or False.

3. Eating eggs will cause high cholesterol.   **True   False**

4. Eggs, yogurt, and nuts are breakfast superfoods.   **True   False**

5. Breakfast is the most important meal of the day.   **True   False**

Fill in the Blank: Write the term that correctly completes the sentence.

   organic, free-range, and grass fed   **protein powder**   **fast carbs**   **corn**   **eggs**

6. Omega-3 fortified, free-range _____ contain *lutein* and *zeaxanthin*, which support eye health, as well as *choline*, which supports brain development and function, including memory.

7. _____ added to fruit and green smoothies makes for a nutritious breakfast.

8. Yogurt, milk, eggs and meat are best when produced using _____ practices.

DAY 6: CLIMB OFF THAT COUCH!

Today's Action Steps:

■ Start a simple activity that you are sure you can do daily.

■ Commit to building this activity into a regular daily habit.

MEALS	GRAINS	VEGETABLES	FRUITS	DAIRY	MEAT	OILS
	Whole grains/slow starches	Organic or on the Clean 15 list (see page 1)	Organic or on the Clean 15 list	Grass-fed omega-3 milk & healthy dairy alternatives	Grass-fed free-range	Coconut or other high-quality oil
Breakfast						
Lunch						
Dinner						

My Healing Foods Log

My Smart Monitoring Results:

Record your smart monitoring results in the chart below.

Smart Monitoring Chart					
Time	Blood Glucose Levels	Insulin Doses	Foods Eaten Before	Recent Activities	Notes About Stress, New Medications, and Emotions

My Daily Activity:

Record your physical activity for the day below.

Activity	Beginning Time	Duration	Comments Include Observations About How You Felt During the Activity and After

My Diabetes-Healing Checklist:

- ❑ Use smart monitoring to track your blood glucose.
- ❑ Swap sodas with diabetes-healing beverages.
- ❑ Eat diabetes-healing fruits and berries.
- ❑ Swap sugar with stevia.
- ❑ Eat a protein-rich breakfast today.
- ❑ Get off the couch and commit to a regular activity.

My Insights for Today:

Think about what you did and how you felt today. What foods did you eat before you took your readings? What were your stress levels like at the time? Were you active before your readings?

Did you start your walking program today? How far and long did you walk? What other type of moderate exercise interests you? How can you arrange your time differently to help you commit to regular exercise? Write your thoughts below.

Test Your Blood Glucose IQ:

Multiple Choice: Circle the letter that best answers the question.

1. Regular activity has the following effects on your body:

    A. Waste and toxins removed from your body.

    B. Oxygen and nutrient pumping to all organs.

    C. Strengthens your immune system.

    D. All of the above.

2. To achieve the best diabetes-healing results, how many minutes of daily activity are needed?

    A. 90.

    B. 60.

    C. 30.

    D. Any of the above.

True or False: For each statement, circle True or False.

3. Moderate activity can help heal diabetes.   **True   False**

4. We humans are creatures of habit.   **True   False**

5. Slow, regular walking is not enough to improve diabetes.   **True   False**

Fill in the Blank: Write the term that correctly completes the sentence.

   habits   **healing**   **walking**   **kaizen**   **physical activity**

6. After diet, regular _____ is the most important tool in controlling your blood glucose levels.

7. Even slow-paced activities such as yoga, tai chi and _____ can improve diabetes.

8. _____ are automatic behaviors and no willpower is needed.

DAY 7: CARBOHYDRATE SWAP

Today's Action Steps:

■ Stop eating fast carbs today.

■ Remove any refined carb foods still in your cupboards and fridge.

■ Prepare all your meals today using whole, fresh foods.

My Healing Foods Log						
MEALS	GRAINS	VEGETABLES	FRUITS	DAIRY	MEAT	OILS
	Whole grains/slow starches	Organic or on the Clean 15 list (see page 1)	Organic or on the Clean 15 list	Grass-fed omega-3 milk & healthy dairy alternatives	Grass-fed free-range	Coconut or other high-quality oil
Breakfast						
Lunch						
Dinner						

Smart Monitoring Results:

Record your smart monitoring results in the chart below.

Time	Blood Glucose Levels	Insulin Doses	Foods Eaten Before	Recent Activities	Notes About Stress, New Medications, and Emotions

Smart Monitoring Chart is the title spanning the top of the above table.

My Daily Activity:

Record your physical activity for the day below.

Activity	Beginning Time	Duration	Comments Include Observations About How You Felt During the Activity and After

My Diabetes-Healing Checklist:

- ❑ Use smart monitoring to track your blood glucose.
- ❑ Swap sodas with diabetes-healing beverages.
- ❑ Eat diabetes-healing fruits and berries.
- ❑ Swap sugar with stevia.
- ❑ Eat a protein-rich breakfast today.
- ❑ Get off the couch and commit to regular activity.
- ❑ Abstain from bread and baked goods.

My Insights for Today:

Think about what you did and how you felt today. What foods did you eat before you took your readings? What were your stress levels like at the time? Were you active before your readings?

Did you empty your fridge and cupboards of processed, refined, and packaged carbs? Which fast carb will be the most difficult for you to give up? What diabetes-healing replacement are you most excited about? Write your thoughts below.

Test Your Blood Glucose IQ

Multiple Choice: Circle the letter that best answers the question.

1. The secret to the successful breaking of carbohydrate cravings is to:

    A. Snack on items from a vending machine.

    B. Skip meals and healthful snacks.

    C. Give into cravings and make exceptions.

    D. Develop an awareness of a rising appetite and the willpower to resist.

2. Fast carbs have the following effects on your body:

    A. Instantly spike blood glucose

    B. Trigger inflammation

    C. Deplete the omega-3's in your body with the omega-6's contained in the item's re-
       fined vegetable oils

    D. All of the above

True or False: For each statement, circle True or False.

3.	Fast carbs are loaded with diabetes-healing fiber.	**True**	**False**
4.	The refined grains in fast carb snacks may trigger hidden allergies.	**True**	**False**
5.	Fast carbs are more healthful than slow carbs.	**True**	**False**

Fill in the Blank: Write the term that correctly completes the sentence.

> **slow carbs**   **delicious**   **fast carbs**   **corn**   *alloxan*

6. When chlorine gas comes into contact with wheat, to forms a byproduct called
    _____, a substance that destroys the insulin-producing function of the
    pancreas.

7. _____ are highly-processed grain products that have a simple, short chain of
    natural sugar molecules that convert quickly into glucose in your bloodstream.

8. _____ contain fiber and other components that slow down the conversion of
    food to glucose in your bloodstream.

DAY 8: ADD DIABETES-HEALING VEGETABLES

Today's Action Steps:

■ Prepare at least two servings of vegetables with each meal.

■ Stock your fridge with vegetables that are particularly high in vitamins and minerals.

■ Eat your fill of veggies without fear of gaining weight!

My Healing Foods Log						
MEALS	**GRAINS**	**VEGETABLES**	**FRUITS**	**DAIRY**	**MEAT**	**OILS**
	Whole grains/slow starches	Organic or on the Clean 15 list (see page 1)	Organic or on the Clean 15 list	Grass-fed omega-3 milk & healthy dairy alternatives	Grass-fed free-range	Coconut or other high-quality oil
Breakfast						
Lunch						
Dinner						

Smart Monitoring Results:

Record your smart monitoring results in the chart below.

Smart Monitoring Chart					
Time	Blood Glucose Levels	Insulin Doses	Foods Eaten Before	Recent Activities	Notes About Stress, New Medications, and Emotions

My Daily Activity:

Record your physical activity for the day below.

Activity	Beginning Time	Duration	Comments Include Observations About How You Felt During the Activity and After

My Diabetes-Healing Checklist:

- ❏ Use smart monitoring to track your blood glucose.
- ❏ Swap sodas with diabetes-healing beverages.
- ❏ Eat diabetes-healing fruits and berries.
- ❏ Swap sugar with stevia.
- ❏ Eat a protein-rich breakfast today.
- ❏ Get off the couch and commit to regular activity.
- ❏ Abstain from bread and baked goods.
- ❏ Eat two servings of vegetables with each meal.

My Insights for Today:

Think about what you did and how you felt today. What foods did you eat before you took your readings? What were your stress levels like at the time? Were you active before your readings?

Plentiful vegetables in your diet will help heal your diabetes. Which vegetables did you prepare today? Which vegetables have been challenging for you to eat in the past, and which are you excited about trying? Write your thoughts below.

_____

_____

_____

_____

_____

_____

_____

_____

_____

Test Your Blood Glucose IQ:

Multiple Choice: Circle the letter that best answers the question.

1. Cruciferous veggies include all of the following except:

   A. Celery

   B. Bok choy

   C. Broccoli

   D. Cabbage

2. *Sulforaphane*, found in cruciferous vegetables, aids which healing process in the body?

   A. Prevents arterial plaque.

   B. Neutralizes oxidative damage done by free radicals.

   C. Preventing blood vessel damage.

   D. Healing blood vessels harmed by inflammation.

True or False: For each statement, circle True or False.

3. Vitamin C can protect against damage done by free radicals and exposure to pollution and toxins.   **True   False**

4. Vitamin A is an antioxidant that is particularly destructive to your eyesight.   **True   False**

5. Folic acid can be found in romaine lettuce, spinach, asparagus, cauliflower, and beans.   **True   False**

Fill in the Blank: Write the term that correctly completes the sentence.

   calories   vitamin C   fiber   corn   toxins

6. Eating your fill of vegetables will not cause weight gain because they are extremely low in _____.

7. Because vegetables are high in _____, they are metabolized slowly and do not spike your blood glucose levels.

8. As the roughage in vegetables passes through and out of your body, it binds to cholesterol, fat, waste products, and _____.

DAY 9: SMART PROTEIN SWAP

Today's Action Steps:

■ Throw away junky protein sources.

■ Purchase organic protein sources, such as grass-fed meats, wild Alaskan salmon, and free-range omega-3 eggs.

MEALS	GRAINS	VEGETABLES	FRUITS	DAIRY	MEAT	OILS
	Whole grains/slow starches	Organic or on the Clean 15 list (see page 1)	Organic or on the Clean 15 list	Grass-fed omega-3 milk & healthy dairy alternatives	Grass-fed free-range	Coconut or other high-quality oil
Breakfast						
Lunch						
Dinner						

My Healing Foods Log

My Smart Monitoring Results:

Record your smart monitoring results in the chart below.

Smart Monitoring Chart					
Time	Blood Glucose Levels	Insulin Doses	Foods Eaten Before	Recent Activities	Notes About Stress, New Medications, and Emotions

My Daily Activity:

Record your physical activity for the day below.

Activity	Beginning Time	Duration	Comments Include Observations About How You Felt During the Activity and After

My Diabetes-Healing Checklist:

❑ Use smart monitoring to track your blood glucose.
❑ Swap sodas with diabetes-healing beverages.
❑ Eat diabetes-healing fruits and berries.
❑ Swap sugar with stevia.
❑ Eat a protein-rich breakfast today.
❑ Get off the couch and commit to a regular activity.
❑ Abstain from bread and baked goods.
❑ Eat two servings of vegetables with each meal.
❑ Eat high-quality protein.

My Insights for Today:

Think about what you did and how you felt today. What foods did you eat before you took your readings? What were your stress levels like at the time? Were you active before your readings?

How did it feel to treat yourself to some high-quality protein? Which types of high-quality protein will you use for your daily breakfast? Write your thoughts below.

_____

_____

_____

_____

_____

_____

_____

_____

_____

_____

Test Your Blood Glucose IQ:

Multiple Choice: Circle the letter that best answers the question.

1. Vegetarians can add protein to their diet with:

    A. Soy

    B. Legumes

    C. Protein powders

    D. All of the above.

2. Which of the following food pairing create a complete protein?

    A. Beans and cornbread

    B. Bread and butter

    C. Hummus and pita bread

    D. A and C

True or False: For each statement, circle True or False.

3. Our bodies need protein to build nerves, tissues, bones, and
    new cells.   **True   False**

4. High-quality meats are filled with hormones, antibiotics,
    preservatives and other chemicals.   **True   False**

5. Protein sources that are preserved or processed will help
    heal your diabetes.   **True   False**

Fill in the Blank: Write the term that correctly completes the sentence.

junky protein   factory farms   fiber   corn   omega-3s

6. Animals in big _____ are fed an unnatural diet to speed up production.

7. Grass-fed beef is high in essential fatty acids and _____.

8. Hotdogs and bologna are examples of _____ sources.

DAY 10: HEALTHY FAT SWAP AND OIL CHANGE

Today's Action Steps:

■ Remove harmful cooking oils in your kitchen and replace them with healthful ones.

■ Eliminate any foods in your pantry or fridge that contain harmful oils.

■ Read labels to become more aware of foods that contain harmful fats.

MEALS	GRAINS	VEGETABLES	FRUITS	DAIRY	MEAT	OILS
	Whole grains/slow starches	Organic or on the Clean 15 list (see page 1)	Organic or on the Clean 15 list	Grass-fed omega-3 milk & healthy dairy alternatives	Grass-fed free-range	Coconut or other high-quality oil
Breakfast						
Lunch						
Dinner						

My Healing Foods Log

My Smart Monitoring Results:

Record your smart monitoring results in the chart below.

Smart Monitoring Chart					
Time	Blood Glucose Levels	Insulin Doses	Foods Eaten Before	Recent Activities	Notes About Stress, New Medications, and Emotions

My Daily Activity:

Record your physical activity for the day below.

Activity	Beginning Time	Duration	Comments Include Observations About How You Felt During the Activity and After

My Diabetes-Healing Checklist:

- ❏ Use smart monitoring to track your blood glucose.
- ❏ Swap sodas with diabetes-healing beverages.
- ❏ Eat diabetes-healing fruits and berries.
- ❏ Swap sugar with stevia.
- ❏ Eat a protein-rich breakfast today.
- ❏ Get off the couch and commit to a regular activity.
- ❏ Abstain from bread and baked goods.
- ❏ Eat two servings of vegetables with each meal.
- ❏ Eat high-quality protein.
- ❏ Swap vegetable oils, margarines, and shortening for healthful oils.

My Insights for Today:

Think about what you did and how you felt today. What foods did you eat before you took your readings? What were your stress levels like at the time? Were you active before your readings?

Did you get rid of all the harmful oils in your kitchen? Which healthful oil is your new favorite? How have your ideas about fats changed as you have progressed through the *30-Day Diabetes Cure*? Write your thoughts below.

_____

_____

_____

_____

_____

_____

_____

_____

Test Your Blood Glucose IQ:

Multiple Choice: Circle the letter that best answers the question.

1.   Organic butter is considered healthful when:

   A. It is consumed with abandon.

   B. It is consumed in moderation.

   C. It is never considered healthful.

   D. None of the above.

2.   The following are healthful fats:

   A. Cold-pressed extra virgin olive oil

   B. Coconut oil

   C. Good ole butter

   D. All of the above

True or False: For each statement, circle True or False.

3.	Organic butter is better for your health than margarine.	True	False
4.	Saturated fats can improve your health if used in moderation.	True	False
5.	Raw seeds and nuts are bad for your health.	True	False

Fill in the Blank: Write the term that correctly completes the sentence.

   cold-pressed   avocado   rBGH   wild caught   smoke point

6.   _____ is a fruit loaded with beneficial fats.

7.   Cold water, _____ Alaskan salmon is a good source of healthful fats.

8.   _____ extra-virgin olive oil is a healthful saturated fat.

DAY 11: EASE STRESS

Today's Action Steps:

■ Prioritize getting a good night's sleep.

■ Reduce as many stress-producing factors in your life as is possible.

MEALS	GRAINS	VEGETABLES	FRUITS	DAIRY	MEAT	OILS
My Healing Foods Log						
	Whole grains/slow starches	Organic or on the Clean 15 list (see page 1)	Organic or on the Clean 15 list	Grass-fed omega-3 milk & healthy dairy alternatives	Grass-fed free-range	Coconut or other high-quality oil
Breakfast						
Lunch						
Dinner						

My Smart Monitoring Results:

Record your smart monitoring results in the chart below.

Smart Monitoring Chart					
Time	Blood Glucose Levels	Insulin Doses	Foods Eaten Before	Recent Activities	Notes About Stress, New Medications, and Emotions

My Daily Activity:

Record your physical activity for the day below.

Activity	Beginning Time	Duration	Comments Include Observations About How You Felt During the Activity and After

My Diabetes-Healing Checklist:

❑ Use smart monitoring to track your blood glucose.

❑ Swap sodas with diabetes-healing beverages.

❑ Eat diabetes-healing fruits and berries.

❑ Swap sugar with stevia.

❑ Eat a protein-rich breakfast today.

❑ Get off the couch and commit to a regular activity.

❑ Abstain from bread and baked goods.

❑ Eat two servings of vegetables with each meal.

❑ Eat high-quality protein.

❑ Swap vegetable oils, margarines, and shortening for healthful oils.

❑ Ease stress.

My Insights for Today:

Think about what you did and how you felt today. What foods did you eat before you took your readings? What were your stress levels like at the time? Were you active before your readings?

Take the time now to write a list of the stressors in your life, big and small. Are there any you can immediately eliminate? How much of your stress is related to a lack of time? Is there a way to lessen the number of time commitments you have? Is there a way to reorganize your time, or even your priorities? Write your thoughts below.

Test Your Blood Glucose IQ:

Multiple Choice: Circle the letter that best answers the question.

1. The best way to deal with stress is to:

    A. Eliminate and reduce as much stress as possible.

    B. Ignore your stress as well as its causes.

    C. Worry constantly about the sources of your stress.

    D. All of the above

2. Higher stress levels affect blood glucose levels in which way?

    A. Higher stress has no effect on blood glucose levels.

    B. Higher stress has a very little effect on blood glucose levels.

    C. Higher stress leads to lower blood glucose levels.

    D. Higher stress leads to higher blood glucose levels.

True or False: For each statement, circle True or False.

3. Sleep deprivation increases insulin resistance.　　　　　　**True   False**

4. Researchers now place stress on par with smoking cigarettes
    in terms of risk for heart disease.　　　　　　　　　　　**True   False**

5. Stress hormones function to ensure that your body has just
    enough glucose available in your bloodstream to be able to
    deal with daily life.　　　　　　　　　　　　　　　　　**True   False**

Fill in the Blank: Write the term that correctly completes the sentence.

　　protein　　　procrastination　　　meditation　　　move　　　out of control

6. Feeling _____ is the underlying basis for most stress.

7. In addition to immediately relaxing you, _____ lowers your heart rate
and blood pressure, reduces the adrenaline and cortisol in your bloodstream, and sharp-
ens your mental functions and creativity.

8. _____ creates extra background stress; it is far less stressful to
deal with issues as they arise.

DAY 12: SMART LUNCH SWAP

Today's Action Steps:

■ Build lunch around lean protein, two vegetables and a healthful fat.

■ Pack tomorrow's lunch tonight.

My Healing Foods Log						
MEALS	**GRAINS**	**VEGETABLES**	**FRUITS**	**DAIRY**	**MEAT**	**OILS**
	Whole grains/slow starches	Organic or on the Clean 15 list (see page 1)	Organic or on the Clean 15 list	Grass-fed omega-3 milk & healthy dairy alternatives	Grass-fed free-range	Coconut or other high-quality oil
Breakfast						
Lunch						
Dinner						

My Smart Monitoring Results:

Record your smart monitoring results in the chart below.

Smart Monitoring Chart					
Time	Blood Glucose Levels	Insulin Doses	Foods Eaten Before	Recent Activities	Notes About Stress, New Medications, and Emotions

My Daily Activity:

Record your physical activity for the day below.

Activity	Beginning Time	Duration	Comments Include Observations About How You Felt During the Activity and After

My Diabetes-Healing Checklist:

❑ Use smart monitoring to track your blood glucose.
❑ Swap sodas with diabetes-healing beverages.
❑ Eat diabetes-healing fruits and berries.
❑ Swap sugar with stevia.
❑ Eat a protein-rich breakfast today.
❑ Get off the couch and commit to a regular activity.
❑ Abstain from bread and baked goods.
❑ Eat two servings of vegetables with each meal.
❑ Eat high-quality protein.
❑ Swap vegetable oils, margarines, and shortening for healthful oils.
❑ Ease stress.
❑ Pack your lunch for tomorrow, and eat a diabetes-healing lunch today.

My Insights for Today:

Think about what you did and how you felt today. What foods did you eat before you took your readings? What were your stress levels like at the time? Were you active before your readings?

What did you prepare for your diabetes-healing lunch today? How did you feel through-out the afternoon after eating your healthful lunch? What are you going to pack for lunch tomorrow? Write your thoughts below.

_____

_____

_____

_____

_____

_____

_____

_____

Test Your Blood Glucose IQ:

Multiple Choice: Circle the letter that best answers the question.

1. Which typical lunch foods are damaging to blood pressure?

    A. Pizza

    B. Hot dogs

    C. Fast food

    D. All of the above

2. The benefits of brown-bagging your lunch are:

    A. No waiting in lines

    B. More time to take a lunch-time walk

    C. Eating food you don't like

    D. A and B

True or False: For each statement, circle True or False.

3. A good way to make sure you pack a lunch is to assemble it
    the night before.   **True   False**

4. Extra-virgin olive oil, organic cheese and avocado are all fat
    sources that will hurt your blood glucose.   **True   False**

5. Vegetables are not slow carbs.   **True   False**

Fill in the Blank: Write the term that correctly completes the sentence.

   cold-pressed   brown-bag   healthful snack   fiber-rich   hard-boiled

6. The ideal lunch includes a lean protein, good fat, and _____
    complex carbohydrate.

7. Making extra food at dinnertime is an easy way to _____ lunch
    the following day.

8. _____ eggs, legumes, wild Alaska salmon, organic beef, bison and
    chicken are all excellent sources of lunchtime protein.

DAY 13: SNACK SENSIBLY

Today's Action Steps:

■ If you must snack, ensure that you choose one combines high-quality protein, vegetables and fiber.

			My Healing Foods Log			
MEALS	**GRAINS**	**VEGETABLES**	**FRUITS**	**DAIRY**	**MEAT**	**OILS**
	Whole grains/slow starches	Organic or on the Clean 15 list (see page 1)	Organic or on the Clean 15 list	Grass-fed omega-3 milk & healthy dairy alternatives	Grass-fed free-range	Coconut or other high-quality oil
Breakfast						
Lunch						
Dinner						

My Smart Monitoring Results:

Record your smart monitoring results in the chart below.

Smart Monitoring Chart					
Time	Blood Glucose Levels	Insulin Doses	Foods Eaten Before	Recent Activities	Notes About Stress, New Medications, and Emotions

My Daily Activity:

Record your physical activity for the day below.

Activity	Beginning Time	Duration	Comments Include Observations About How You Felt During the Activity and After

My Diabetes-Healing Checklist:

- ❏ Use smart monitoring to track your blood glucose.
- ❏ Swap sodas with diabetes-healing beverages.
- ❏ Eat diabetes-healing fruits and berries.
- ❏ Swap sugar with stevia.
- ❏ Eat a protein-rich breakfast today.
- ❏ Get off the couch and commit to a regular activity.
- ❏ Abstain from bread and baked goods.
- ❏ Eat two servings of vegetables with each meal.
- ❏ Eat high-quality protein.
- ❏ Swap vegetable oils, margarines, and shortening for healthful oils.
- ❏ Ease stress.
- ❏ Pack your lunch for tomorrow, and eat a diabetes-healing lunch today.
- ❏ Make sensible choices if you must have a snack.

My Insights for Today:

Think about what you did and how you felt today. What foods did you eat before you took your readings? What were your stress levels like at the time? Were you active before your readings?

Did you feel genuinely hungry and in need of a snack between meals today? What healthful snack did you reach for? Write your thoughts below.

_____

_____

_____

_____

_____

_____

_____

Test Your Blood Glucose IQ:

Multiple Choice: Circle the letter that best answers the question.

1.   The perfect snack combines which of the following?

    A. Quality protein

    B. Healthful fat

    C. Slow carb

    D. All of the above

2.   A snack should contain:

    A. As many calories as possible

    B. 200-250 calories

    C. No more than 100-150 calories

    D. None of the above

True or False: For each statement, circle True or False.

3.	Nuts, fruit and yogurt make an ideal snack.	**True**	**False**
4.	Junky snacks can masquerade as health food.	**True**	**False**
5.	Snacking is absolutely necessary.	**True**	**False**

Fill in the Blank: Write the term that correctly completes the sentence.

Fat   chips   refined carbohydrates   refried beans   cinnamon

6.   When your meals contain _____ insulin levels spike and you will want to snack.

7.   Raw vegetables can be dipped in warm, vegetarian _____.

8.   A blood glucose-friendly snack substitution for a bag of _____ is air-popped popcorn with olive oil and Parmesan cheese.

DAY 14: RESPOND, INSTEAD OF REACT

Today's Action Steps:

■ Practice slowing down and collecting yourself before you speak.

■ Resist the impulse to react.

My Healing Foods Log						
MEALS	**GRAINS**	**VEGETABLES**	**FRUITS**	**DAIRY**	**MEAT**	**OILS**
	Whole grains/slow starches	Organic or on the Clean 15 list (see page 1)	Organic or on the Clean 15 list	Grass-fed omega-3 milk & healthy dairy alternatives	Grass-fed free-range	Coconut or other high-quality oil
Breakfast						
Lunch						
Dinner						

My Smart Monitoring Results:

Record your smart monitoring results in the chart below.

Smart Monitoring Chart					
Time	Blood Glucose Levels	Insulin Doses	Foods Eaten Before	Recent Activities	Notes About Stress, New Medications, and Emotions

My Daily Activity:

Record your physical activity for the day below.

Activity	Beginning Time	Duration	Comments Include Observations About How You Felt During the Activity and After

My Diabetes-Healing Checklist:

❑ Use smart monitoring to track your blood glucose.

❑ Swap sodas with diabetes-healing beverages.

❑ Eat diabetes-healing fruits and berries.

❑ Swap sugar with stevia.

❑ Eat a protein-rich breakfast today.

❑ Get off the couch and commit to a regular activity.

❑ Abstain from bread and baked goods.

❑ Eat two servings of vegetables with each meal.

❑ Eat high-quality protein.

❑ Swap vegetable oils, margarines, and shortening for healthful oils.

❑ Ease stress.

❑ Pack your lunch for tomorrow, and eat a diabetes-healing lunch today.

❑ Make sensible choices if you must have a snack.

❑ Respond, don't react.

My Insights for Today:

Think about what you did and how you felt today. What foods did you eat before you took your readings? What were your stress and activity levels like? Were you active before you took your readings?

Do you find yourself responding or reacting in stressful situations? How do you typically deal with stressful situations in your daily life? How can you modify your own behaviors in order to interact with others in a more positive way? How do you think this will benefit you? Write your thoughts below.

_____

_____

_____

_____

_____

_____

_____

_____

_____

_____

_____

_____

_____

_____

_____

Test Your Blood Glucose IQ:

Multiple Choice: Circle the letter that best answers the question.

1. Learn to give yourself time to cool down by:

    A. Observing

    B. Breathing

    C. Counting

    D. All of the above

2. To interrupt the reactive cycle, which of the following questions is useful:

    A. Why are they doing this to me?

    B. Am I crazy?

    C. Am I reacting?

    D. All of the above

True or False: For each statement, circle True or False.

3. In situations of conflict, you do not always have to give
    someone an immediate answer.   **True   False**

4. Even professionals can do nothing to help a reactive person
    change their behavior.   **True   False**

5. Counseling can help you manage your feelings and figure out
    the real reason for your anger.   **True   False**

Fill in the Blank: Write the term that correctly completes the sentence.

facts   mental rehearsal   behavioral   reactive emotions   slow down

6. Hesitation techniques can help you _____and collect yourself
    before you speak.

7. _____ can help you balance out reactive emotions by
    providing you with a set of responses to use in the future.

8. _____ interfere with your ability to think clearly.

DAY 15: STEP UP YOUR ACTIVITY LEVEL

Today's Action Steps:

■ Incorporate two new activities into your daily routine.

■ Get up and move every hour.

■ Add more distance and difficulty to your current fitness routine.

■ Talk to your doctor about your plans for raising your activity level.

My Healing Foods Log						
MEALS	**GRAINS**	**VEGETABLES**	**FRUITS**	**DAIRY**	**MEAT**	**OILS**
	Whole grains/slow starches	Organic or on the Clean 15 list (see page 1)	Organic or on the Clean 15 list	Grass-fed omega-3 milk & healthy dairy alternatives	Grass-fed free-range	Coconut or other high-quality oil
Breakfast						
Lunch						
Dinner						

My Smart Monitoring Results:

Record your smart monitoring results in the chart below.

Time	Blood Glucose Levels	Insulin Doses	Foods Eaten Before	Recent Activities	Notes About Stress, New Medications, and Emotions

My Daily Activity:

Record your physical activity for the day below.

Activity	Beginning Time	Duration	Comments Include Observations About How You Felt During the Activity and After

My Diabetes-Healing Checklist:

❑ Use smart monitoring to track your blood glucose.

❑ Swap sodas with diabetes-healing beverages.

❑ Eat diabetes-healing fruits and berries.

❑ Swap sugar with stevia.

❑ Eat a protein-rich breakfast today.

❑ Get off the couch and commit to a regular activity.

❑ Abstain from bread and baked goods.

❑ Eat two servings of vegetables with each meal.

❑ Eat high-quality protein.

❑ Swap vegetable oils, margarines, and shortening for healthful oils.

❑ Ease stress.

❑ Pack your lunch for tomorrow, and eat a diabetes-healing lunch today.

❑ Make sensible choices if you must have a snack.

❑ Respond, don't react.

❑ Add more distance and difficulty to your current fitness routine.

My Insights for Today:

Think about what you did and how you felt today. What foods did you eat before you took your readings? What were your stress levels like at the time? Were you active before your readings?

What is your current daily activity? Has your ability to complete this activity improved as you've increased your strength? In what way do you want to increase the distance or intensity of your exercise routine? Is there another activity you are interested in trying now that your confidence and ability has increased? Write your thoughts below.

Test Your Blood Glucose IQ:

Multiple Choice: Circle the letter that best answers the question.

1. You can make your current exercise routine more intense by:

   A. Adding hills or stairs to your route

   B. Carrying light weights

   C. Adding more distance

   D. All of the above

2. New exercises to try that will increase your heart rate include:

   A. Water-walking and spin classes

   B. Going to the movies weekly

   C. Watching the newest television series

   D. None of the above

True or False: For each statement, circle True or False.

3. Date nights should always be quiet, sedentary affairs.　　**True　False**

4. Your doctor can't help you decide which activities are safe for you.　　**True　False**

5. Walking in a pool puts less stress on your heart than walking on land. .　　**True　False**

Fill in the Blank: Write the term that correctly completes the sentence.

calories　　　**routine chores**　　　**dance**　　　**exert**　　　**movement**

6. Date nights can be opportunities for _____ when you skip the movie and instead skate, hike, or dance.

7. _____ such as sweeping, mopping, and vacuuming are opportunities to increase your daily activity level.

8. The more you _____ your body, the stronger and more capable it becomes.

DAY 16: CONQUER SELF-SABOTAGE

Today's Action Steps:

■ Practice positive self-talk today.

■ Make one small change in your routine to break an unhealthful habit.

			My Healing Foods Log			
MEALS	**GRAINS**	**VEGETABLES**	**FRUITS**	**DAIRY**	**MEAT**	**OILS**
	Whole grains/slow starches	Organic or on the Clean 15 list (see page 1)	Organic or on the Clean 15 list	Grass-fed omega-3 milk & healthy dairy alternatives	Grass-fed free-range	Coconut or other high-quality oil
Breakfast						
Lunch						
Dinner						

My Smart Monitoring Results:

Record your smart monitoring results in the chart below.

Smart Monitoring Chart					
Time	Blood Glucose Levels	Insulin Doses	Foods Eaten Before	Recent Activities	Notes About Stress, New Medications, and Emotions

My Daily Activity:

Record your physical activity for the day below.

Activity	Beginning Time	Duration	Comments Include Observations About How You Felt During the Activity and After

My Diabetes-Healing Checklist:

❑ Use smart monitoring to track your blood glucose.

❑ Swap sodas with diabetes-healing beverages.

❑ Eat diabetes-healing fruits and berries.

❑ Swap sugar with stevia.

❑ Eat a protein-rich breakfast today.

❑ Get off the couch and commit to a regular activity.

❑ Abstain from bread and baked goods.

❑ Eat two servings of vegetables with each meal.

❑ Eat high-quality protein.

❑ Swap vegetable oils, margarines, and shortening for healthful oils.

❑ Ease stress.

❑ Pack your lunch for tomorrow, and eat a diabetes-healing lunch today.

❑ Make sensible choices if you must have a snack.

❑ Respond, don't react.

❑ Add more distance and difficulty to your current fitness routine.

❑ Conquer self-sabotage.

My Insights for Today:

Think about what you did and how you felt today. What foods did you eat before you took your readings? What were your stress and activity levels like? Were you active before you took your readings?

How well have you been sticking to the 30-Day Plan? Do you find yourself making excuses and exceptions? Write down a positive affirmation that will encourage you to embrace this healthful lifestyle. What is one habit you are going to break today? Write your thoughts below.

Test Your Blood Glucose IQ:

Multiple Choice: Circle the letter that best answers the question.

1. Which sentence below is an example of positive self-talk:

    A. "I'm healing my diabetes with every step I walk."

    B. "I'm healthier with every sip of this delicious smoothie."

    C. "I feel happy with my decision to stick with this plan."

    D. All of the above

2. Positive self-talk involves transforming:

    A. Positive thoughts into negative thoughts

    B. Negative thoughts into positive thoughts

    C. Talking to yourself constantly

    D. All of the above

True or False: For each statement, circle True or False.

3. You can help keep yourself motivated by tracking your progress and planning out your week.   **True   False**

4. Making lots of exceptions to your diet will not sabotage your diabetes-healing regime.   **True   False**

5. Self-sabotages to avoid include sneaking treats, not asking for support, and not getting enough sleep.   **True   False**

Fill in the Blank: Write the term that correctly completes the sentence.

accountable   meal planning   behavioral   sabotage   re-motivate

6. To stick with your new lifestyle, it is important to _____ yourself regularly.

7. _____ helps you avoid fast-carb, high-sugar eating.

8. Being _____ to a friend lets you tell them about your new diet and lifestyle and ask for a reminder when they notice you reverting to an unhealthful habit.

DAY 17: ELIMINATE TOXIC FOOD INGREDIENTS

Today's Action Steps:

■ Throw away food with toxic ingredients.

■ Buy real food the next time you go shopping.

■ "Vote" with your dollars and refuse to buy foods that contain toxic ingredients.

My Healing Foods Log						
MEALS	**GRAINS**	**VEGETABLES**	**FRUITS**	**DAIRY**	**MEAT**	**OILS**
	Whole grains/slow starches	Organic or on the Clean 15 list	Organic or on the Clean 15 list	Grass-fed omega-3 milk & healthy dairy alternatives	Grass-fed free-range	Coconut or other high-quality oil
Breakfast						
Lunch						
Dinner						

My Smart Monitoring Results:

Record your smart monitoring results in the chart below.

Smart Monitoring Chart					
Time	Blood Glucose Levels	Insulin Doses	Foods Eaten Before	Recent Activities	Notes About Stress, New Medications, and Emotions

My Daily Activity:

Record your physical activity for the day below.

Activity	Beginning Time	Duration	Comments Include Observations About How You Felt During the Activity and After

My Diabetes-Healing Checklist:

- ❏ Use smart monitoring to track your blood glucose.
- ❏ Swap sodas with diabetes-healing beverages.
- ❏ Eat diabetes-healing fruits and berries.
- ❏ Swap sugar with stevia.
- ❏ Eat a protein-rich breakfast today.
- ❏ Get off the couch and commit to a regular activity.
- ❏ Abstain from bread and baked goods.
- ❏ Eat two servings of vegetables with each meal.
- ❏ Eat high-quality protein.
- ❏ Swap vegetable oils, margarines, and shortening for healthful oils.
- ❏ Ease stress.
- ❏ Pack your lunch for tomorrow, and eat a diabetes-healing lunch today.
- ❏ Make sensible choices if you must have a snack.
- ❏ Respond, don't react.
- ❏ Add more distance and difficulty to your current fitness routine.
- ❏ Conquer self-sabotage.
- ❏ Skip food containing toxic ingredients.

My Insights for Today:

Think about what you did and how you felt today. What foods did you eat before you took your readings? What were your stress levels like at the time? Were you active before your readings?

Which of the Top 10 worst toxic food ingredients did you find in the foods in your kitchen? What sorts of foods will you shop for in order to avoid consuming these toxic ingredients? Write your thoughts below.

_____

_____

_____

_____

_____

Test Your Blood Glucose IQ:

Multiple Choice: Circle the letter that best answers the question.

1. Whole foods include:

   A. Fresh and frozen organically grown vegetables.

   B. Meat and eggs that are cage-free, free range and pasture-raised.

   C. Dairy products that are labeled "organic" and hormone-free.

   D. All of the above

2. Sodium nitrite and nitrate are chemicals commonly used to preserve:

   A. Dried meats, lunch meats and canned meats.

   B. Milk and dairy products

   C. Chips

   D. None of the above

True or False: For each statement, circle True or False.

3. Shortening and margarine are great for your health.   **True   False**

4. The omega-6 fatty acids in refined oils neutralize the benefits of omega-3s in your diet.   **True   False**

5. When you boycott certain foods, it helps to get the attention of food manufacturers.   **True   False**

Fill in the Blank: Write the term that correctly completes the sentence.

vegetable oils   potassium bromate   rBGH   nitrites   nitrates   aspartame

6. Canola, soybean, corn, safflower, and peanut are all examples of harmful, refined _____.

7. Salami, corned beef, pate, and smoked salmon most likely contain unhealthful _____ and _____.

8. The toxic ingredient _____ is an additive used to increase the volume in some flours, breads, and baked goods.

DAY 18: EAT MORE BEANS AND LEGUMES

Today's Action Steps:

■ Eat more beans and legumes than usual today.

■ Incorporate beans into breakfast and snack time.

My Healing Foods Log						
MEALS	**GRAINS**	**VEGETABLES**	**FRUITS**	**DAIRY**	**MEAT**	**OILS**
	Whole grains/slow starches	Organic or on the Clean 15 list (see page 1)	Organic or on the Clean 15 list	Grass-fed omega-3 milk & healthy dairy alternatives	Grass-fed free-range	Coconut or other high-quality oil
Breakfast						
Lunch						
Dinner						

My Smart Monitoring Results:

Record your smart monitoring results in the chart below.

Smart Monitoring Chart					
Time	Blood Glucose Levels	Insulin Doses	Foods Eaten Before	Recent Activities	Notes About Stress, New Medications, and Emotions

My Daily Activity:

Record your physical activity for the day below.

Activity	Beginning Time	Duration	Comments Include Observations About How You Felt During the Activity and After

My Diabetes-Healing Checklist:

❑ Use smart monitoring to track your blood glucose.
❑ Swap sodas with diabetes-healing beverages.
❑ Eat diabetes-healing fruits and berries.
❑ Swap sugar with stevia.
❑ Eat a protein-rich breakfast today.
❑ Get off the couch and commit to a regular activity.
❑ Abstain from bread and baked goods.
❑ Eat two servings of vegetables with each meal.
❑ Eat high-quality protein.
❑ Swap vegetable oils, margarines, and shortening for healthful oils.
❑ Ease stress.
❑ Pack your lunch for tomorrow, and eat a diabetes-healing lunch today.
❑ Make sensible choices if you must have a snack.
❑ Respond, don't react.
❑ Add more distance and difficulty to your current fitness routine.
❑ Conquer self-sabotage.
❑ Skip food containing toxic ingredients.
❑ Add more beans and legumes to your meals and snacks.

My Insights for Today:

Think about what you did and how you felt today. What foods did you eat before you took your readings? What were your stress levels like at the time? Were you active before your readings?

How do you feel about adding more beans and legumes to your diet? Which legumes will you chose to stock in your diabetes-healing kitchen? What are some ways you can prepare these powerful healing agents? Write your thoughts below.

_____

_____

_____

_____

_____

_____

_____

_____

_____

_____

_____

_____

_____

_____

_____

Test Your Blood Glucose IQ:

Multiple Choice: Circle the letter that best answers the question.

1. Beans and legumes can be eaten:

   A. For breakfast

   B. For lunch and dinner

   C. For snack

   D. All of the above

2. Although homemade is better, canned beans are an acceptable alternative if:

   A. You otherwise wouldn't eat beans

   B. You feel cooking beans is too involved

   C. They contain no more than 300-400 mg of sodium

   D. All of the above

True or False: For each statement, circle True or False.

3. Beans are one of the worst foods you can eat to heal
   your diabetes.   **True   False**

4. Garbanzo beans are the main ingredients in hummus dip.   **True   False**

5. Edamame is difficult to prepare as it involves boiling the
   pod and sprinkling it with salt.   **True   False**

Fill in the Blank: Write the term that correctly completes the sentence.

container   blood glucose   comfort foods   edamame   crockpot

6. _____ are green soybeans that grow as pods with peas inside and
   are harvested while still young.

7. Beans can be sorted and soaked overnight, followed by slow cooking them in a
   _____ the next day.

8. Beans and legumes can lower _____, blood pressure, your weight
   and your grocery bill.

DAY 19: PRACTICE CONSCIOUS DINING

Today's Action Steps:

■ Slow down when you eat today.

■ Use all five senses at every meal.

My Healing Foods Log						
MEALS	**GRAINS**	**VEGETABLES**	**FRUITS**	**DAIRY**	**MEAT**	**OILS**
	Whole grains/slow starches	Organic or on the Clean 15 list (see page 1)	Organic or on the Clean 15 list	Grass-fed omega-3 milk & healthy dairy alternatives	Grass-fed free-range	Coconut or other high-quality oil
Breakfast						
Lunch						
Dinner						

My Smart Monitoring Results:

Record your smart monitoring results in the chart below.

Smart Monitoring Chart					
Time	Blood Glucose Levels	Insulin Doses	Foods Eaten Before	Recent Activities	Notes About Stress, New Medications, and Emotions

My Daily Activity:

Record your physical activity for the day below.

Activity	Beginning Time	Duration	Comments Include Observations About How You Felt During the Activity and After

My Diabetes-Healing Checklist:

❑ Use smart monitoring to track your blood glucose.

❑ Swap sodas with diabetes-healing beverages.

❑ Eat diabetes-healing fruits and berries.

❑ Swap sugar with stevia.

❑ Eat a protein-rich breakfast today.

❑ Get off the couch and commit to a regular activity.

❑ Abstain from bread and baked goods.

❑ Eat two servings of vegetables with each meal.

❑ Eat high-quality protein.

❑ Swap vegetable oils, margarines, and shortening for healthful oils.

❑ Ease stress.

❑ Pack your lunch for tomorrow, and eat a diabetes-healing lunch today.

❑ Make sensible choices if you must have a snack.

❑ Respond, don't react.

❑ Add more distance and difficulty to your current fitness routine.

❑ Conquer self-sabotage.

❑ Skip food containing toxic ingredients.

❑ Add more beans and legumes to your meals and snacks.

❑ Practice conscious dining by engaging all five senses.

My Insights for Today:

Think about what you did and how you felt today. What foods did you eat before you took your readings? How were your stress levels? Were you active before your readings?

Look at your dining table right now and describe how it looks and what is on it. Is it an inviting and stress-free place to enjoy your meals? What can you do to make your dining space more inviting? Write your thoughts below.

_____

_____

_____

_____

_____

_____

_____

_____

_____

_____

_____

_____

_____

_____

_____

_____

Test Your Blood Glucose IQ:

Multiple Choice: Circle the letter that best answers the question.

1. An inviting dining environment includes:

    A. Homework, bills, and random papers

    B. A tablecloth, candles, and flowers

    C. Placemats, special dishes and music

    D. B and C

2. To recognize when you are full:

    A. Place a hand on your stomach, close your eyes, and breathe deeply.

    B. See how you feel after eating seconds.

    C. Check to see if you've cleaned your plate.

    D. All of the above

True or False: For each statement, circle True or False.

3. Conscious dining helps slow down your meal and avoid overeating.   **True   False**

4. Eating in the car, at a desk or while walking around means you will enjoy your food more and eat less.   **True   False**

5. Eating and dining are the same thing.   **True   False**

Fill in the Blank: Write the term that correctly completes the sentence.

enjoyable   20–30   comfort foods   atmosphere   flowers

6. Relax before eating because you want to avoid reaching for _____ to soothe emotions.

7. One of the benefits of slow, conscious dining is a more _____ meal.

8. Slow down and try to make your meal last for _____ minutes.

DAY 20: CONSIDER A DETOX PROGRAM

Today's Action Steps:

■ Drink plenty of pure water in order to support your body's natural detox system.

■ Supplement your body's detox system with milk thistle and turmeric.

■ Eat tons of fiber to maintain good elimination of toxins.

\multicolumn{7}{c}{My Healing Foods Log}						
MEALS	**GRAINS**	**VEGETABLES**	**FRUITS**	**DAIRY**	**MEAT**	**OILS**
	Whole grains/slow starches	Organic or on the Clean 15 list (see page 1)	Organic or on the Clean 15 list	Grass-fed omega-3 milk & healthy dairy alternatives	Grass-fed free-range	Coconut or other high-quality oil
Breakfast						
Lunch						
Dinner						

My Smart Monitoring Results:

Record your smart monitoring results in the chart below.

Smart Monitoring Chart					
Time	Blood Glucose Levels	Insulin Doses	Foods Eaten Before	Recent Activities	Notes About Stress, New Medications, and Emotions

My Daily Activity:

Record your physical activity for the day below.

Activity	Beginning Time	Duration	Comments Include Observations About How You Felt During the Activity and After

My Diabetes-Healing Checklist:

❑ Use smart monitoring to track your blood glucose.
❑ Swap sodas with diabetes-healing beverages.
❑ Eat diabetes-healing fruits and berries.
❑ Swap sugar with stevia.
❑ Eat a protein-rich breakfast today.
❑ Get off the couch and commit to a regular activity.
❑ Abstain from bread and baked goods.
❑ Eat two servings of vegetables with each meal.
❑ Eat high-quality protein.
❑ Swap vegetable oils, margarines, and shortening for healthful oils.
❑ Ease stress.
❑ Pack your lunch for tomorrow, and eat a diabetes-healing lunch today.
❑ Make sensible choices if you must have a snack.
❑ Respond, don't react.
❑ Add more distance and difficulty to your current fitness routine.
❑ Conquer self-sabotage.
❑ Skip food containing toxic ingredients.
❑ Add more beans and legumes to your meals and snacks.
❑ Practice conscious dining by engaging all five senses.
❑ Support your body's natural detox system by eating fiber and drinking plenty of water.

My Insights for Today:

Think about what you did and how you felt today. What foods did you eat before you took your readings? What were your stress levels like at the time? Were you active before your readings?

After reading through Day 20 of the *30-Day Diabetes Cure*, how would you describe a healthful detox program? What are you already doing to cleanse your body? How can you continue to support your body's natural detox system? Write your thoughts below.

Test Your Blood Glucose IQ:

Multiple Choice: Circle the letter that best answers the question.

1. Fad detox programs and fasting regimes are harmful to diabetics because:

    A. They remove toxins from the body.

    B. They can cause long-term damage.

    C. They dramatically disturb the metabolism.

    D. B and C

2. Common symptoms accompanying detoxification include:

    A. Mild skin rash

    B. Nausea

    C. Temporary fatigue

    D. All of the above

True or False: For each statement, circle True or False.

3. Toxins are present in our food, water, soil, and air. **True   False**

4. Blood leaving the stomach and intestines flows first to the
    liver for detoxification. **True   False**

5. Skin only absorbs toxins into the body. **True   False**

Fill in the Blank: Write the term that correctly completes the sentence.

turmeric   skin   comfort foods   milk thistle   flowers

6. Your body's largest organ, the _____, can release toxins via sweat
    and oil glands.

7. _____ protects the liver from damage and helps it regenerate
    healthy cells.

8. The Ayurvedic herb _____ speeds the flow of bile and its toxic load.

DAY 21: SLEEP LONGER AND BETTER

Today's Action Steps:

■ Remove any objects from your bedroom that might disrupt your sleep.

■ Prepare for a good night's sleep by rearranging your pre-bedtime routine.

				My Healing Foods Log		
MEALS	**GRAINS**	**VEGETABLES**	**FRUITS**	**DAIRY**	**MEAT**	**OILS**
	Whole grains/slow starches	Organic or on the Clean 15 list (see page 1)	Organic or on the Clean 15 list	Grass-fed omega-3 milk & healthy dairy alternatives	Grass-fed free-range	Coconut or other high-quality oil
Breakfast						
Lunch						
Dinner						

My Smart Monitoring Results:

Record your smart monitoring results in the chart below.

Smart Monitoring Chart					
Time	Blood Glucose Levels	Insulin Doses	Foods Eaten Before	Recent Activities	Notes About Stress, New Medications, and Emotions

My Daily Activity:

Record your physical activity for the day below.

Activity	Beginning Time	Duration	Comments Include Observations About How You Felt During the Activity and After

My Diabetes-Healing Checklist:

- ❑ Use smart monitoring to track your blood glucose.
- ❑ Swap sodas with diabetes-healing beverages.
- ❑ Eat diabetes-healing fruits and berries.
- ❑ Swap sugar with stevia.
- ❑ Eat a protein-rich breakfast today.
- ❑ Get off the couch and commit to a regular activity.
- ❑ Abstain from bread and baked goods.
- ❑ Eat two servings of vegetables with each meal.
- ❑ Eat high-quality protein.
- ❑ Swap vegetable oils, margarines, and shortening for healthful oils.
- ❑ Ease stress.
- ❑ Pack your lunch for tomorrow, and eat a diabetes-healing lunch today.
- ❑ Make sensible choices if you must have a snack.
- ❑ Respond, don't react.
- ❑ Add more distance and difficulty to your current fitness routine.
- ❑ Conquer self-sabotage.
- ❑ Skip food containing toxic ingredients.
- ❑ Add more beans and legumes to your meals and snacks.
- ❑ Practice conscious dining by engaging all five senses.
- ❑ Support your body's natural detox system by eating fiber and drinking plenty of water.
- ❑ Modify your bedtime habits so you sleep longer and better.

My Insights for Today:

Think about what you did and how you felt today. What foods did you eat before you took your readings? What were your stress levels like at the time? Were you active before your readings?

Is your bedroom ready for a healthful night's sleep? Do you need to change your bedtime routine for a better night's sleep? Write your thoughts below.

Beginning here, record your sleep patterns from the previous night. Include how many hours of uninterrupted sleep, if you had any difficulty falling asleep, or if your sleep was disrupted in any way. Note any sleep-related issues from the previous day. (See page 308 of *The 30-Day Diabetes Cure.*)

Test Your Blood Glucose IQ:

Multiple Choice: Circle the letter that best answers the question.

1. For a better night's sleep, begin winding down:

   A. Five minutes before bedtime

   B. As early as possible

   C. At least one hour before bed time

   D. None of the above

2. Which of the following can contribute to difficulty falling asleep?

   A. Watching the news just before bed

   B. Computer time just before bedtime

   C. Exercising too late in the evening

   D. All of the above

True or False: For each statement, circle True or False.

3. Adequate amounts of sleep diminish brain function and mood.   **True**   **False**

4. Quality sleep heals your diabetes.   **True**   **False**

5. For the best sleep possible, your bedroom should be loaded
   with televisions, phones, computers, and other electronic devices.   **True**   **False**

Fill in the Blank: Write the term that correctly completes the sentence.

   heated conversations   **sleepy**   **immune system**   **sleep apnea**
   prescription sleeping pills

6. Next-day drowsiness, depression, memory loss and addiction are some of the side
   effects of _____ .

7. To help induce relaxation, keep the bedroom peaceful and avoid _____ before
   bedtime.

8. If you snore, are overweight, and your partner or spouse says you stop breathing
   during the night, then you might have _____.

DAY 22: ADD YOGA

Today's Action Steps:

■ Find a yoga class to get you started on a regular practice.

■ Begin a daily practice of yoga.

MEALS	GRAINS	VEGETABLES	FRUITS	DAIRY	MEAT	OILS
	Whole grains/slow starches	Organic or on the Clean 15 list (see page 1)	Organic or on the Clean 15 list	Grass-fed omega-3 milk & healthy dairy alternatives	Grass-fed free-range	Coconut or other high-quality oil
Breakfast						
Lunch						
Dinner						

My Healing Foods Log

My Smart Monitoring Results:

Record your smart monitoring results in the chart below.

Smart Monitoring Chart					
Time	Blood Glucose Levels	Insulin Doses	Foods Eaten Before	Recent Activities	Notes About Stress, New Medications, and Emotions

My Daily Activity:

Record your physical activity for the day below.

Activity	Beginning Time	Duration	Comments Include Observations About How You Felt During the Activity and After

My Diabetes-Healing Checklist:

❑ Use smart monitoring to track your blood glucose.

❑ Swap sodas with diabetes-healing beverages.

❑ Eat diabetes-healing fruits and berries.

❑ Swap sugar with stevia.

❑ Eat a protein-rich breakfast today.

❑ Get off the couch and commit to a regular activity.

❑ Abstain from bread and baked goods.

❑ Eat two servings of vegetables with each meal.

❑ Eat high-quality protein.

❑ Swap vegetable oils, margarines, and shortening for healthful oils.

❑ Ease stress.

❑ Pack your lunch for tomorrow, and eat a diabetes-healing lunch today.

❑ Make sensible choices if you must have a snack.

❑ Respond, don't react.

❑ Add more distance and difficulty to your current fitness routine.

❑ Conquer self-sabotage.

❑ Skip food containing toxic ingredients.

❑ Add more beans and legumes to your meals and snacks.

❑ Practice conscious dining by engaging all five senses.

❑ Support your body's natural detox system by eating fiber and drinking plenty of water.

❑ Modify your bedtime habits so you sleep longer and better.

❑ Practice yoga in a class or on your own.

My Insights for Today:

Think about what you did and how you felt today. What foods did you eat before you took your readings? What were your stress levels like at the time? Were you active before your readings?

Have you ever tried the healing practice of yoga? How did you feel after giving it a try for the first time? In what way can you incorporate yoga into your daily routine? Write your thoughts below.

Record last night's sleep patterns (see page 91).

_____

_____

_____

_____

_____

_____

_____

_____

_____

_____

_____

_____

_____

_____

Test Your Blood Glucose IQ:

Multiple Choice: Circle the letter that best answers the question.

1. The physical benefits of yoga include:

    A. Stress relief

    B. Muscle toning

    C. Increased flexibility

    D. All of the above

2. The mental benefits of yoga include:

    A. Banished depression

    B. Improved attention and awareness

    C. Balanced hormones and blood chemistry that boost mood and energy

    D. All of the above

True or False: For each statement, circle True or False.

3. Avoid upside-down postures that can increase pressure in
    the eyes if you have retinopathy.   **True   False**

4. Yoga can lower fasting glucose as well as after-meal glucose.   **True   False**

5. The vagus nerve, when stimulated by yoga, increases your
    heart rate significantly and increases stress.   **True   False**

Fill in the Blank: Write the term that correctly completes the sentence.

asanas   read labels   "mindful movement"   wheat   vagus nerve

6. Various _____, or movements and postures, serve to stimulate different
    organs.

7. Yoga movements stimulate the _____, which is responsible for
    controlling your heart rate, breathing, and entire digestive system.

8. Yoga is a gentle, _____ practice.

DAY 23: REDUCE DEPRESSION AND BOREDOM

Today's Action Steps:

■ Increase your consumption of depression-healing foods today.

■ Plan an activity that makes you feel good.

My Healing Foods Log						
MEALS	**GRAINS**	**VEGETABLES**	**FRUITS**	**DAIRY**	**MEAT**	**OILS**
	Whole grains/slow starches	Organic or on the Clean 15 list	Organic or on the Clean 15 list	Grass-fed omega-3 milk & healthy dairy alternatives	Grass-fed free-range	Coconut or other high-quality oil
Breakfast						
Lunch						
Dinner						

My Smart Monitoring Results:

Record your smart monitoring results in the chart below.

Smart Monitoring Chart					
Time	Blood Glucose Levels	Insulin Doses	Foods Eaten Before	Recent Activities	Notes About Stress, New Medications, and Emotions

My Daily Activity:

Record your physical activity for the day below.

Activity	Beginning Time	Duration	Comments Include Observations About How You Felt During the Activity and After

My Diabetes-Healing Checklist:

❑ Use smart monitoring to track your blood glucose.

❑ Swap sodas with diabetes-healing beverages.

❑ Eat diabetes-healing fruits and berries.

❑ Swap sugar with stevia.

❑ Eat a protein-rich breakfast today.

❑ Get off the couch and commit to a regular activity.

❑ Abstain from bread and baked goods.

❑ Eat two servings of vegetables with each meal.

❑ Eat high-quality protein.

❑ Swap vegetable oils, margarines, and shortening for healthful oils.

❑ Ease stress.

❑ Pack your lunch for tomorrow, and eat a diabetes-healing lunch today.

❑ Make sensible choices if you must have a snack.

❑ Respond, don't react.

❑ Add more distance and difficulty to your current fitness routine.

❑ Conquer self-sabotage.

❑ Skip food containing toxic ingredients.

❑ Add more beans and legumes to your meals and snacks.

❑ Practice conscious dining by engaging all five senses.

❑ Support your body's natural detox system by eating fiber and drinking plenty of water.

❑ Modify your bedtime habits so you sleep longer and better.

❑ Practice yoga in a class or on your own.

❑ Take steps to reduce depression and boredom.

My Insights for Today:

Think about what you did and how you felt today. What foods did you eat before you took your readings? What were your stress levels like? Were you active before your readings?

Do you feel that you are depressed or bored at times? What depression-healing foods did you try today? What activity did you do to elevate your mood? Are any aspects of your new lifestyle helping? Write your thoughts below.

Record last night's sleep patterns (see page 91).

_____

_____

_____

_____

_____

_____

_____

_____

_____

_____

_____

_____

_____

_____

_____

Test Your Blood Glucose IQ:

Multiple Choice: Circle the letter that best answers the question.

1. Many people feel better when they:

    A. Get outside for some sun and exercise

    B. Eat fast carbs

    C. Spend time with family and friends

    D. A and C

2. Which of the following can you do to alleviate depression and boredom?

    A. Develop negative inner narratives

    B. Volunteer

    C. Get less sleep

    D. All of the above

True or False: For each statement, circle True or False.

3. Spending time with animals can help reduce feeling of
   depression and boredom.   **True   False**

4. Tryptophan is an essential amino acid that elevates serotonin
   levels in the brain.   **True   False**

5. Watching loads of television can help you feel less depressed
   and bored.   **True   False**

Fill in the Blank: Write the term that correctly completes the sentence.

depression-healing   power   breathing exercises   increasing   decreasing

6. Omega-3s, tryptophan, B vitamins, calcium, and magnesium are all considered
   _____ foods.

7. Depression exacerbate your diabetes by _____ your stress and
   anxiety levels.

8. Every positive action you take increases your _____ to create more
   happiness for yourself and others.

DAY 24: ADD A SUPPORT SYSTEM

Today's Action Steps:

■ Find an existing diabetes support group and attend a meeting.

■ Call a friend or family member today, talk to them about your plan to heal your diabetes, and ask for their support.

My Healing Foods Log						
MEALS	**GRAINS**	**VEGETABLES**	**FRUITS**	**DAIRY**	**MEAT**	**OILS**
	Whole grains/slow starches	Organic or on the Clean 15 list (see page 1)	Organic or on the Clean 15 list	Grass-fed omega-3 milk & healthy dairy alternatives	Grass-fed free-range	Coconut or other high-quality oil
Breakfast						
Lunch						
Dinner						

My Smart Monitoring Results:

Record your smart monitoring results in the chart below.

Smart Monitoring Chart					
Time	Blood Glucose Levels	Insulin Doses	Foods Eaten Before	Recent Activities	Notes About Stress, New Medications, and Emotions

My Daily Activity:

Record your physical activity for the day below.

Activity	Beginning Time	Duration	Comments Include Observations About How You Felt During the Activity and After

My Diabetes-Healing Checklist:

❑ Use smart monitoring to track your blood glucose.

❑ Swap sodas with diabetes-healing beverages.

❑ Eat diabetes-healing fruits and berries.

❑ Swap sugar with stevia.

❑ Eat a protein-rich breakfast today.

❑ Get off the couch and commit to a regular activity.

❑ Abstain from bread and baked goods.

❑ Eat two servings of vegetables with each meal.

❑ Eat high-quality protein.

❑ Swap vegetable oils, margarines, and shortening for healthful oils.

❑ Ease stress.

❑ Pack your lunch for tomorrow, and eat a diabetes-healing lunch today.

❑ Make sensible choices if you must have a snack.

❑ Respond, don't react.

❑ Add more distance and difficulty to your current fitness routine.

❑ Conquer self-sabotage.

❑ Skip food containing toxic ingredients.

❑ Add more beans and legumes to your meals and snacks.

❑ Practice conscious dining by engaging all five senses.

❑ Support your body's natural detox system by eating fiber and drinking plenty of water.

❑ Modify your bedtime habits so you sleep longer and better.

❑ Practice yoga in a class or on your own.

❑ Take steps to reduce depression and boredom.

❑ Connect with your support system today.

My Insights for Today:

Think about what you did and how you felt today. What foods did you eat before you took your readings? What were your stress levels like? Were you active before you took your readings?

Are you going to seek out a diabetes support group and enlist the help of your family and friends? Which will be the most difficult part of asking for this help? Which part will be the most rewarding and beneficial? Write your thoughts below.

Record last night's sleep patterns (see page 91).

Test Your Blood Glucose IQ:

Multiple Choice: Circle the letter that best answers the question.

1. When setting up your own support system, remember to:

    A. Be honest about how diabetes is affecting you.

    B. Make your needs known.

    C. Ask for support for your new diet and lifestyle .

    D. Do all of the above.

2. Which of the following are signs of a safe, effective diabetes support group?

    A. High cost to join.

    B. Promise of fast, easy solutions and quick cures.

    C. Pushing you to abandon medical treatment.

    D. None of the above.

True or False: For each statement, circle True or False.

3. Diabetes is an incurable condition.   True   False

4. Diabetes can make you feel isolated and alone.   True   False

5. Counseling can propel you toward new ways of interacting
   with friends and family.   True   False

Fill in the Blank: Write the term that correctly completes the sentence.

> **support groups**   **need**   **veterans**   **newcomers**   **leave**

6. Since not all the information you ay receive at a support group meeting will be immediately relevant to you, take what you _____ and _____ the rest.

7. _____ can help end isolation, boost motivation, and provide peer support.

8. The best support groups will have a balance of _____ and _____ who will provide different perspectives on the process of managing and healing diabetes.

107

DAY 25: REDUCE YOUR EXPOSURE TO ENVIRONMENTAL TOXINS

Today's Action Steps:

■ Gather up the toxic cleaning supplies in your home.

■ Take these toxic industrial chemicals to your recycling center for disposal.

MEALS	GRAINS	VEGETABLES	FRUITS	DAIRY	MEAT	OILS
	Whole grains/slow starches	Organic or on the Clean 15 list (see page 1)	Organic or on the Clean 15 list	Grass-fed omega-3 milk & healthy dairy alternatives	Grass-fed free-range	Coconut or other high-quality oil
Breakfast						
Lunch						
Dinner						

My Healing Foods Log

My Smart Monitoring Results:

Record your smart monitoring results in the chart below.

Smart Monitoring Chart					
Time	Blood Glucose Levels	Insulin Doses	Foods Eaten Before	Recent Activities	Notes About Stress, New Medications, and Emotions

My Daily Activity:

Record your physical activity for the day below.

Activity	Beginning Time	Duration	Comments Include Observations About How You Felt During the Activity and After

My Diabetes-Healing Checklist:

❑ Use smart monitoring to track your blood glucose.

❑ Swap sodas with diabetes-healing beverages.

❑ Eat diabetes-healing fruits and berries.

❑ Swap sugar with stevia.

❑ Eat a protein-rich breakfast today.

❑ Get off the couch and commit to a regular activity.

❑ Abstain from bread and baked goods.

❑ Eat two servings of vegetables with each meal.

❑ Eat high-quality protein.

❑ Swap vegetable oils, margarines, and shortening for healthful oils.

❑ Ease stress.

❑ Pack your lunch for tomorrow, and eat a diabetes-healing lunch today.

❑ Make sensible choices if you must have a snack.

❑ Respond, don't react.

❑ Add more distance and difficulty to your current fitness routine.

❑ Conquer self-sabotage.

❑ Skip food containing toxic ingredients.

❑ Add more beans and legumes to your meals and snacks.

❑ Practice conscious dining by engaging all five senses.

❑ Support your body's natural detox system by eating fiber and drinking plenty of water.

❑ Modify your bedtime habits so you sleep longer and better.

❑ Practice yoga in a class or on your own.

❑ Take steps to reduce depression and boredom.

❑ Connect with your support system today.

❑ Clear toxins from your immediate environment.

My Insights for Today:

Think about what you did and how you felt today. What foods did you eat before you took your readings? What were your stress and activity levels like? Were you active before you took your readings?

What sort of toxins do you think will be the most difficult for you to avoid? How have you been helping your body's natural detox system, and how can you boost its power even more? Write your thoughts below.

Record last night's sleep patterns (see page 91).

_____

_____

_____

_____

_____

_____

_____

_____

_____

_____

_____

_____

_____

_____

Test Your Blood Glucose IQ:

Multiple Choice: Circle the letter that best answers the question.

1. You can help reduce the toxins in your home when you:

    A. Pitch plastics

    B. Go with glass

    C. Use conventional cleaning supplies

    D. A and B

2. Persistent organic pollutants (POPs) can be found in:

    A. Water and air

    B. Household cleaners, shampoos and lotions

    C. Food

    D. All of the above

True or False: For each statement, circle True or False.

3. Because they can be transported by wind and water, most POPs generated in one area affect people and wildlife far from where they are used and released.   **True   False**

4. A high-quality water filter will not remove pesticides, pharmaceuticals, and other impurities from your drinking water.   **True   False**

5. Antibiotics, growth hormones, pesticides, and fungicides are all examples of persistent organic pollutants.   **True   False**

Fill in the Blank: Write the term that correctly completes the sentence.

detoxing   fake scent   dangerous   POPs   toxic chemicals

6. Persistent organic pollutants are also known as _____.

7. When ridding your house of toxins, it's important to remove anything with a _____ including air fresheners, scented dryer sheets, lotions, and candles.

8. Processed foods and factory meats are a major source of _____.

112

DAY 26: ADD VITAMINS AND SUPPLEMENTS

Today's Action Steps:

■ Buy a multivitamin and vitamin D.

■ Gradually expand this basic supplement program according to your needs.

My Healing Foods Log						
MEALS	**GRAINS**	**VEGETABLES**	**FRUITS**	**DAIRY**	**MEAT**	**OILS**
	Whole grains/slow starches	Organic or on the Clean 15 list (see page 1)	Organic or on the Clean 15 list	Grass-fed omega-3 milk & healthy dairy alternatives	Grass-fed free-range	Coconut or other high-quality oil
Breakfast						
Lunch						
Dinner						

My Smart Monitoring Results:

Record your smart monitoring results in the chart below.

Smart Monitoring Chart					
Time	Blood Glucose Levels	Insulin Doses	Foods Eaten Before	Recent Activities	Notes About Stress, New Medications, and Emotions

My Daily Activity:

Record your physical activity for the day below.

Activity	Beginning Time	Duration	Comments Include Observations About How You Felt During the Activity and After

My Diabetes-Healing Checklist:

❑ Use smart monitoring to track your blood glucose.

❑ Swap sodas with diabetes-healing beverages.

❑ Eat diabetes-healing fruits and berries.

❑ Swap sugar with stevia.

❑ Eat a protein-rich breakfast today.

❑ Get off the couch and commit to a regular activity.

❑ Abstain from bread and baked goods.

❑ Eat two servings of vegetables with each meal.

❑ Eat high-quality protein.

❑ Swap vegetable oils, margarines, and shortening for healthful oils.

❑ Ease stress.

❑ Pack your lunch for tomorrow, and eat a diabetes-healing lunch today.

❑ Make sensible choices if you must have a snack.

❑ Respond, don't react.

❑ Add more distance and difficulty to your current fitness routine.

❑ Conquer self-sabotage.

❑ Skip food containing toxic ingredients.

❑ Add more beans and legumes to your meals and snacks.

❑ Practice conscious dining by engaging all five senses.

❑ Support your body's natural detox system by eating fiber and drinking plenty of water.

❑ Modify your bedtime habits so you sleep longer and better.

❑ Practice yoga in a class or on your own.

❑ Take steps to reduce depression and boredom.

❑ Connect with your support system today.

❑ Clear toxins from your immediate environment.

❑ Take diabetes-healing vitamins and supplements.

My Insights for Today:

Think about what you did and how you felt today. What foods did you eat before you took your readings? What were your stress and activity levels like? Were you active before you took your readings?

Which vitamins and supplements would you like to start taking? Do you plan to consult your doctor about a new vitamin and supplement regimen? Write your thoughts below.

Record last night's sleep patterns (see page 91).

_____

_____

_____

_____

_____

_____

_____

_____

_____

_____

_____

_____

_____

_____

Test Your Blood Glucose IQ:

Multiple Choice: Circle the letter that best answers the question.

1. One-a-day multivitamins contain nutrient levels based on:

    A. Recommended daily allowances

    B. Optimal levels for your specific needs

    C. Minimal levels to avoid nutritional deficiency diseases

    D. A and C

2. The most effective vitamins and supplements will:

    A. Be extremely inexpensive.

    B. Contain natural, absorbable forms of vitamins and minerals.

    C. Be based on a popular gimmick, such as "liquid" and "whole food" vitamins.

    D. All of the above

True or False: For each statement, circle True or False.

3. Even the most balanced of diets does not offer all of the vitamins and minerals necessary for optimal health.   **True   False**

4. Vitamin D deficiency is the leading nutritional deficiency in our nation.   **True   False**

5. Vitamin and supplement producers are well regulated by the government, so there is no need to look for third-party reviewer labels.   **True   False**

Fill in the Blank: Write the term that correctly completes the sentence.

     calcium   supplement program   dangerous   minimum   coleus forskohlii

6. Your basic _____ should include vitamin D, vitamin C, L-arginine, and magnesium.

7. Taking a _____ of 1–2,000 IU of vitamin D3 on days when you have no sun exposure will improve your insulin resistance.

8. Chlorella and _____ are other supplements that can help improve your diabetes.

DAY 27: BECOME A VOLUNTEER

Today's Action Steps:

■ Investigate volunteer opportunities in your area.

■ Make an appointment to meet the people involved.

MEALS	GRAINS	VEGETABLES	FRUITS	DAIRY	MEAT	OILS
	Whole grains/slow starches	Organic or on the Clean 15 list (see page 1)	Organic or on the Clean 15 list	Grass-fed omega-3 milk & healthy dairy alternatives	Grass-fed free-range	Coconut or other high-quality oil
Breakfast						
Lunch						
Dinner						

My Healing Foods Log

My Smart Monitoring Results:

Record your smart monitoring results in the chart below.

Smart Monitoring Chart					
Time	Blood Glucose Levels	Insulin Doses	Foods Eaten Before	Recent Activities	Notes About Stress, New Medications, and Emotions

My Daily Activity:

Record your physical activity for the day below.

Activity	Beginning Time	Duration	Comments Include Observations About How You Felt During the Activity and After

My Diabetes-Healing Checklist:

- ❑ Use smart monitoring to track your blood glucose.
- ❑ Swap sodas with diabetes-healing beverages.
- ❑ Eat diabetes-healing fruits and berries.
- ❑ Swap sugar with stevia.
- ❑ Eat a protein-rich breakfast today.
- ❑ Get off the couch and commit to a regular activity.
- ❑ Abstain from bread and baked goods.
- ❑ Eat two servings of vegetables with each meal.
- ❑ Eat high-quality protein.
- ❑ Swap vegetable oils, margarines, and shortening for healthful oils.
- ❑ Ease stress.
- ❑ Pack your lunch for tomorrow, and eat a diabetes-healing lunch today.
- ❑ Make sensible choices if you must have a snack.
- ❑ Respond, don't react.
- ❑ Add more distance and difficulty to your current fitness routine.
- ❑ Conquer self-sabotage.
- ❑ Skip food containing toxic ingredients.
- ❑ Add more beans and legumes to your meals and snacks.
- ❑ Practice conscious dining by engaging all five senses.
- ❑ Support your body's natural detox system by eating fiber and drinking plenty of water.
- ❑ Modify your bedtime habits so you sleep longer and better.
- ❑ Practice yoga in a class or on your own.
- ❑ Take steps to reduce depression and boredom.
- ❑ Connect with your support system today.
- ❑ Clear toxins from your immediate environment.
- ❑ Take diabetes-healing vitamins and supplements.
- ❑ Volunteer your time and skills to help others.

My Insights for Today:

Think about what you did and how you felt today. What foods did you eat before you took your readings? What were your stress levels like at the time? Were you active before your readings?

How do you feel about volunteering? What benefits do you think you could receive as well as provide? What do you think is a reasonable amount of time for you to volunteer? Brainstorm a list of places or people you might like to volunteer for and write your thoughts below.

Record last night's sleep patterns (see page 91).

Test Your Blood Glucose IQ:

Multiple Choice: Circle the letter that best answers the question.

1.   Volunteers often reap the following benefits:

   A. Pleasure, feeling connected, and enhanced people skills.

   B. Less time for things that matter to them.

   C. It costs money to volunteer.

   D. None of the above.

2.   Which of the following are worthy volunteer causes?

   A. Teaching an adult to read.

   B. Becoming a foster parent or donating toys to children in foster care.

   C. Walking a dog at the animal shelter.

   D. All of the above.

True or False: For each statement, circle True or False.

3.   Volunteering only benefits those who receive the help.   **True   False**

4.   You could lose the positive benefits of volunteering if you over-commit yourself.   **True   False**

5.   A reasonable volunteer schedule will benefit both you and the receiver.   **True   False**

Fill in the Blank: Write the term that correctly completes the sentence.

   mind   attentive   behavioral   emotional   good

6.   Helping others makes you feel _____ and conquers loneliness, anger, and negativity that lead to high blood pressure or make it worse.

7.   Having a sense of connection to the world outside your door is one of the contributing factors togood mental, _____ and physical health.

8.   Volunteering keeps your _____ sharp, because you are usually learning new skills in the process.

DAY 28: START BUILDING MORE MUSCLE

Today's Action Steps:

■ Purchase light weights and begin using them today.

■ Sign up for a strength training class or a fitness trainer for more direction.

MEALS	GRAINS	VEGETABLES	FRUITS	DAIRY	MEAT	OILS
	Whole grains/slow starches	Organic or on the Clean 15 list (see page 1)	Organic or on the Clean 15 list	Grass-fed omega-3 milk & healthy dairy alternatives	Grass-fed free-range	Coconut or other high-quality oil
Breakfast						
Lunch						
Dinner						

My Healing Foods Log

My Smart Monitoring Results:

Record your smart monitoring results in the chart below.

Smart Monitoring Chart					
Time	Blood Glucose Levels	Insulin Doses	Foods Eaten Before	Recent Activities	Notes About Stress, New Medications, and Emotions

My Daily Activity:

Record your physical activity for the day below.

Activity	Beginning Time	Duration	Comments Include Observations About How You Felt During the Activity and After

My Diabetes-Healing Checklist:

- ❏ Use smart monitoring to track your blood glucose.
- ❏ Swap sodas with diabetes-healing beverages.
- ❏ Eat diabetes-healing fruits and berries.
- ❏ Swap sugar with stevia.
- ❏ Eat a protein-rich breakfast today.
- ❏ Get off the couch and commit to a regular activity.
- ❏ Abstain from bread and baked goods.
- ❏ Eat two servings of vegetables with each meal.
- ❏ Eat high-quality protein.
- ❏ Swap vegetable oils, margarines, and shortening for healthful oils.
- ❏ Ease stress.
- ❏ Pack your lunch for tomorrow, and eat a diabetes-healing lunch today.
- ❏ Make sensible choices if you must have a snack.
- ❏ Respond, don't react.
- ❏ Add more distance and difficulty to your current fitness routine.
- ❏ Conquer self-sabotage.
- ❏ Skip food containing toxic ingredients.
- ❏ Add more beans and legumes to your meals and snacks.
- ❏ Practice conscious dining by engaging all five senses.
- ❏ Support your body's natural detox system by eating fiber and drinking plenty of water.
- ❏ Modify your bedtime habits so you sleep longer and better.
- ❏ Practice yoga in a class or on your own.
- ❏ Take steps to reduce depression and boredom.
- ❏ Connect with your support system today.
- ❏ Clear toxins from your immediate environment.
- ❏ Take diabetes-healing vitamins and supplements.
- ❏ Volunteer your time and skills to help others.
- ❏ Challenge your muscles by lifting light weights.

My Insights for Today:

Think about what you did and how you felt today. What foods did you eat before you took your readings? What were your stress levels like? Were you active before you took your readings?

How did it feel to complete a set of muscle-strengthening repetitions? What are the most important benefits you expect to receive by strengthening your muscles? Write your thoughts below.

Record last night's sleep patterns (see page 91).

Test Your Blood Glucose IQ:

Multiple Choice: Circle the letter that best answers the question.

1. The most effective way to increase your fitness is to:

    A. Only exercise when your friend wants to as well.

    B. Find an activity you love and will stick with.

    C. Force yourself to stick to an exercise routine that is boring or stressful.

    D. None of the above

2. Tips for successful strength training include the following except:

    A. Plan ahead

    B. Hire a trainer

    C. Rest and relax

    D. Skip classes or exercise sessions

True or False: For each statement, circle True or False.

3. Overtraining causes your body to go into shock and lock up fat cells.   **True   False**

4. Having muscles lowers the amount of calories your body burns throughout the day.   **True   False**

5. Resistance training is the use of weights, or some other resistance, to build muscle and increase strength.   **True   False**

Fill in the Blank: Write the term that correctly completes the sentence.

    intensity   short-term recovery   20 points   aerobic exercise   routine

6. Combine strength training with _____ to increase your fitness most effectively.

7. Change your exercise _____ or change its _____ in order to stay motivated, interested and excited.

8. During the _____ period, muscles, tendons, and ligaments are being repaired.

DAY 29: ADD TRAVEL, RESTAURANTS, AND PARTIES

Today's Action Steps:

■ Make a list of local restaurants that specialize in healthful fare.

■ Make a dinner reservation.

My Healing Foods Log						
MEALS	**GRAINS**	**VEGETABLES**	**FRUITS**	**DAIRY**	**MEAT**	**OILS**
	Whole grains/slow Starches	Organic or on the Clean 15 list (see page 1)	Organic or on the Clean 15 list	Grass-fed omega-3 milk & healthy dairy alternatives	Grass-fed free-range	Coconut or other high-quality oil
Breakfast						
Lunch						
Dinner						

My Smart Monitoring Results:

Record your smart monitoring results in the chart below.

Smart Monitoring Chart					
Time	Blood Glucose Levels	Insulin Doses	Foods Eaten Before	Recent Activities	Notes About Stress, New Medications, and Emotions

My Daily Activity:

Record your physical activity for the day below.

Activity	Beginning Time	Duration	Comments Include Observations About How You Felt During the Activity and After

My Diabetes-Healing Checklist:

- ❏ Use smart monitoring to track your blood glucose.
- ❏ Swap sodas with diabetes-healing beverages.
- ❏ Eat diabetes-healing fruits and berries.
- ❏ Swap sugar with stevia.
- ❏ Eat a protein-rich breakfast today.
- ❏ Get off the couch and commit to a regular activity.
- ❏ Abstain from bread and baked goods.
- ❏ Eat two servings of vegetables with each meal.
- ❏ Eat high-quality protein.
- ❏ Swap vegetable oils, margarines, and shortening for healthful oils.
- ❏ Ease stress.
- ❏ Pack your lunch for tomorrow, and eat a diabetes-healing lunch today.
- ❏ Make sensible choices if you must have a snack.
- ❏ Respond, don't react.
- ❏ Add more distance and difficulty to your current fitness routine.
- ❏ Conquer self-sabotage.
- ❏ Skip food containing toxic ingredients.
- ❏ Add more beans and legumes to your meals and snacks.
- ❏ Practice conscious dining by engaging all five senses.
- ❏ Support your body's natural detox system by eating fiber and drinking plenty of water.
- ❏ Modify your bedtime habits so you sleep longer and better.
- ❏ Practice yoga in a class or on your own.
- ❏ Take steps to reduce depression and boredom.
- ❏ Connect with your support system today.
- ❏ Clear toxins from your immediate environment.
- ❏ Take diabetes-healing vitamins and supplements.
- ❏ Volunteer your time and skills to help others.
- ❏ Challenge your muscles by lifting light weights.
- ❏ Add travel and parties.

My Insights for Today:

Think about what you did and how you felt today. What foods did you eat before you took your readings? What were your stress levels like at the time? Were you active before your readings?

Do you find yourself giving in to temptations when at parties and restaurants? What are some new skills you've learned to stay healthy even while at restaurants, on travel and at parties? How do you think this will change your social experiences? Write your thoughts below.

Record last night's sleep patterns (see page 91).

_____

_____

_____

_____

_____

_____

_____

_____

_____

_____

_____

_____

_____

_____

Test Your Blood Glucose IQ:

Multiple Choice: Circle the letter that best answers the question.

1. You should start each meal with:

   A. Soup

   B. Salad

   C. Soup and Salad

   D. None of the above

2. A healthful main course at a restaurant:

   A. Is built around a lean protein with lots of vegetables

   B. Is built around the foods you most crave at the time

   C. Will not taste good

   D. All of the above

True or False: For each statement, circle True or False.

3. If there is a restaurant that represents your old life, it is best to avoid it.   True   False

4. The biggest key to dining-out is your choice of restaurant.   True   False

5. It is very easy to find a healthy meal at a fast-food joint.   True   False

Fill in the Blank: Write the term that correctly completes the sentence.

| **mind** | **locally grown** | **cruise ships** | **vegetables** | **good** |

6. You can stick to good habits at parties as long as you focus on _____ and lean meats.

7. Restaurants that specialize in healthful meals will most likely serve _____, organic produce, pasture-raised meats and wild-caught fish.

8. _____ offer plenty of opportunities to be active, including swimming pools, climbing walls and dances.

DAY 30: CELEBRATE!

Today's Action Steps:

■ Treat today like the special day it is.

■ Plan an outing, gift, or special time for yourself.

				My Healing Foods Log		
MEALS	**GRAINS**	**VEGETABLES**	**FRUITS**	**DAIRY**	**MEAT**	**OILS**
	Whole grains/slow starches	Organic or on the Clean 15 list (see page 1)	Organic or on the Clean 15 list	Grass-fed omega-3 milk & healthy dairy alternatives	Grass-fed free-range	Coconut or other high-quality oil
Breakfast						
Lunch						
Dinner						

My Smart Monitoring Results:

Record your smart monitoring results in the chart below.

Smart Monitoring Chart					
Time	Blood Glucose Levels	Insulin Doses	Foods Eaten Before	Recent Activities	Notes About Stress, New Medications, and Emotions

My Daily Activity:

Record your physical activity for the day below.

Activity	Beginning Time	Duration	Comments Include Observations About How You Felt During the Activity and After

Checklist

- ❏ Use smart monitoring to track your blood glucose.
- ❏ Swap sodas with diabetes-healing beverages.
- ❏ Eat diabetes-healing fruits and berries.
- ❏ Swap sugar with stevia.
- ❏ Eat a protein-rich breakfast today.
- ❏ Get off the couch and commit to a regular activity.
- ❏ Abstain from bread and baked goods.
- ❏ Eat two servings of vegetables with each meal.
- ❏ Eat high-quality protein.
- ❏ Swap vegetable oils, margarines, and shortening for healthful oils.
- ❏ Ease stress.
- ❏ Pack your lunch for tomorrow, and eat a diabetes-healing lunch today.
- ❏ Make sensible choices if you must have a snack.
- ❏ Respond, don't react.
- ❏ Add more distance and difficulty to your current fitness routine.
- ❏ Conquer self-sabotage.
- ❏ Skip food containing toxic ingredients.
- ❏ Add more beans and legumes to your meals and snacks.
- ❏ Practice conscious dining by engaging all five senses.
- ❏ Support your body's natural detox system by eating fiber and drinking plenty of water.
- ❏ Modify your bedtime habits so you sleep longer and better.
- ❏ Practice yoga in a class or on your own.
- ❏ Take steps to reduce depression and boredom.
- ❏ Connect with your support system today.
- ❏ Clear toxins from your immediate environment.
- ❏ Take diabetes-healing vitamins and supplements.
- ❏ Volunteer your time and skills to help others.
- ❏ Challenge your muscles by lifting light weights.
- ❏ Add travel and parties.
- ❏ CELEBRATE!

My Insights for Today:

Have your blood glucose levels normalized over the last 30 days? Did you lose weight, add muscle, increase your energy level or improve your mood? What's the best thing that happened to you on The 30-Day Diabetes Cure Plan? Write your thoughts below.

Record last night's sleep patterns (see page 91).

_____

_____

_____

_____

_____

_____

_____

_____

_____

_____

_____

_____

_____

_____

_____

_____

Test Your Blood Glucose IQ:

Multiple Choice: Circle the letter that best answers the question.

1. You can celebrate your new, healthy lifestyle by:

    A. Eating whatever you want

    B. Buying yourself a gift

    C. Making a date with yourself and doing something special

    D. B and C

2. Remind yourself that your diabetes will:

    A. Stay the same

    B. Go downhill

    C. Heal as you continue to implement what you've done these past 30 days.

    D. None of the above

True or False: For each statement, circle True or False.

3. You are feeling better now than you have in years.   **True**   **False**

4. Today is a day to rejoice in all the wonderful new things you have done for yourself.   **True**   **False**

5. You can celebrate by meditating, taking a walk, dressing-up, and eating well before you even leave the house.

    True   **False**

Fill in the Blank: Write the term that correctly completes the sentence.

mind   30 days   something special   tools   good

6. If you could change this much in just _____, imagine how your life can look even better six months from now, a year from now, ten years from now!

7. Whether you work today or not, plan to do _____ either during the day, on your lunch break, or after work.

8. You have learned skills and _____ that will continue to improve your life.

Answer Key

Day 1 1. C, **2.** D, **3.** F, **4.** T, **5.** T, **6.** testing in pairs, **7.** logging, **8.** blood glucose levels

Day 2 1. C, **2.** B, **3.** T, **4.** F, 5. T, **6.** nutritional value, **7.** pomegranate, **8.** glucose load

Day 3 1. D, **2.** B, **3.** T, **4.** F, **5.** T, **6.** diabetes-healing, **7.** free radicals, **8.** fruit, avoid

Day 4 1. B, **2.** D, **3.** F, **4.** T, **5.** F, **6.** fuel, 7. appetite, **8.** hunger

Day 5 1. C, **2.** D, **3.** F, **4.** T, **5.** T, **6.** eggs, **7.** protein powder, **8.** organic, free-range, and grass-fed

Day 6 1. D, **2.** C, **3.** T, **4.** T, **5.** F, **6.** physical activity, **7.** walking, **8.** habits

Day 7 1. D, **2.** D, **3.** F, **4.** T, **5.** T, **6.** alloxan, **7.** fast carbs, **8.** slow carbs

Day 8 1. A, **2.** D, **3.** T, **4.** F, **5.** T, **6.** calories, **7.** fiber, **8.** toxins

Day 9 1. D, **2.** D, **3.** T, **4.** F, **5.** F, **6.** factory farms, **7.** omega-3s, **8.** junky protein

Day 10 1. B, **2.** D, **3.** T, **4.** T, **5.** F, **6.** avocado, **7.** wild caught, **8.** cold-pressed

Day 11 1. A, **2.** D, **3.** T, **4.** T, **5.** F, **6.** out of control, **7.** meditation, **8.** procrastination

Day 12 1. D, **2.** D, **3.** T, **4.** F, **5.** F, **6.** fiber-rich, **7.** brown bag, **8.** hard-boiled

Day 13 1. D, **2.** C, **3.** T, **4.** T, **5.** F, **6.** refined carbohydrates, **7.** refried beans, **8.** chips

Day 14 1. D, **2.** C, **3.** T, **4.** F, **5.** T, **6.** slow down, **7.** mental rehearsal, **8.** reactive emotions

Day 15 1. D, **2.** A, **3.** F, **4.** F, **5.** T, **6.** movement, **7.** routine chores, **8.** exert

Day 16 1. D, **2.** B, **3.** T, **4.** F, **5.** T, **6.** re-motivate, **7.** meal planning, **8.** accountable

Day 17 1. D, **2.** A, **3.** F, **4.** T, **5.** T, **6.** vegetable oils, **7.** nitrates, nitrites, **8.** potassium bromate

Day 18 1. D, **2.** D, **3.** F, **4.** T, **5.** F, **6.** edamame, **7.** crockpot, **8.** blood glucose

Day 19 1. D, **2.** A, **3.** T, **4.** F, **5.** F, **6.** comfort foods, **7.** enjoyable, **8.** 20–30

Day 20 1. D, **2.** D, **3.** T, **4.** T, **5.** F, **6.** skin, **7.** milk thistle, **8.** turmeric

Day 21 1. C, **2.** D, **3.** F, **4.** T, **5.** F, **6.** prescription sleeping pills, **7.** heated conversations, **8.** sleep apnea

Day 22 1. D, **2.** D, **3.** T, **4.** T, **5.** F, **6.** asanas, **7.** vagus nerve, **8.** "mindful movement"

Day 23 1. D, **2.** B, **3.** T **4.** T, **5.** F, **6.** depression-healing, **7.** increasing, **8.** power

Day 24 1. D, **2.** D, **3.** F, **4.** T, **5.** T, **6.** need, leave, **7.** support groups, **8.** newcomers, veterans

Day 25 1. D, **2.** D, **3.** T, **4.** F, **5.** T, **6.** POPs, **7.** fake scent, **8.** toxic chemicals

Day 26 1. D, **2.** B, **3.** T, **4.** T, **5.** F, **6.** supplement program, **7.** minimum, **8.** coleus forskohlii

Day 27 1. A, **2.** D, **3.** F, **4.** T, **5.** F, **6.** good, **7.** emotional, **8.** mind

Day 28 1. B, **2.** D, **3.** T, **4.** F, **5.** T, **6.** aerobic exercise, **7.** routine, intensity, **8.** short-term recovery

Day 29 1. C, **2.** A, **3.** T, **4.** T, **5.** F, **6.** vegetables, **7.** locally grown, **8.** cruise ships

Day 30 1. D, **2.** C, **3.** T, **4.** T, **5.** T, **6.** 30 days, **7.** something special, **8.** tools